Surrendered Sleep:
A Biblical Perspective

Turning your heart to God
while facing sleep disorders and insomnia

by

Charles W. Page, M.D.

Surrendered Sleep: A Biblical Perspective
© 2011 Charles W. Page, M.D.

All Scripture quotations, unless otherwise indicated, are taken from the Holy Bible, New International Version®. NIV®. Copyright © 1973, 1978, 1984 by International Bible Society. Used by permission of Zondervan. All rights reserved.

Scripture quotations denoted by KJV are taken from the King James Version of the Bible.

Scripture quotations denoted by ASV are taken from the American Standard Version of the Bible.

Scripture quotations denoted by CJB are taken from the Complete Jewish Bible, Copyright © 1998 by David H. Stern and published by Jewish New Testament Publications, Inc., Clarksville, Maryland. All rights reserved.

Scripture quotations denoted by NAS are taken from The New American Standard Bible, © Copyright 1960, 1962, 1963, 1968, 1971, 1972, 1973, 1975, 1977, 1995 by the Lockman Foundation. Used by permission.

Scripture quotations denoted by CEV are taken from the Contemporary English Version, © Copyright 1991, 1992, 1995 by the American Bible Society. Used by permission. All rights reserved.

Scripture quotations denoted by NKJV are taken from the New King James Version, © Copyright 1982 by Thomas Nelson, Inc. Used by permission. All rights reserved.

ISBN 0983138109 (paperback version)
ISBN 978-0-9831381-0-5 (paperback version)

To my mother
Linda Page

Nothing – not even cancer – can separate you from the love of God.

I found Dr. Page's Surrendered Sleep *fascinating as I had never thought about a biblical connection with sleep. From his own personal issues with sleep, Dr. Page researched how spirituality affects our sleep patterns. Good quality sleep is a problem for so many people, as our lives have become so demanding. Dr. Page brings together the physical, mental, scientific and spiritual aspects of sleep in a way you've not seen before. This book is a must read for everyone, since we all know someone who has a problem sleeping. But, just be ready to lose a little sleep yourself as you find you can't put the book down!*

Brenda Fried
Author
Bridging the Gap of Faith
Shreveport, Louisiana

The spiritual aspects of insomnia have been overlooked by the medical community for too long. While medications have their role for some, they are probably overused in the treatment of insomnia. Surrendered Sleep *explores the root causes of many sleep disturbances from a biblical perspective. Dr. Page offers practical advice on how to draw closer to God to overcome the anxieties and fears that rob many of their night's rest. It is easy to read and biblically sound. I wish I had had a copy sooner for my patients. This book is long overdue!*

Jeffery J Vrielink, M.D.
Christian Psychiatrist
Grand Rapids, Michigan

Have you ever wondered what the Christian faith has to say about sleep? Surrendered Sleep *offers an encouraging and practical approach for those suffering with sleep issues. This book will not only challenge your attitudes regarding sleep disorders and insomnia, but will motivate you to pursue the One who created your need for sleep. You'll want to keep a copy close to your bedside!*

Harold G. Koenig, M.D.
Professor Psychiatry and Behavioral Sciences
Associate Professor of Medicine
Director, Center for Spirituality, Theology and Health
Duke University Medical Center
Durham, North Carolina

Dr. Page cuts through the deceits of modern life to expose the roots of our sleeplessness. His masterful, insightful study of sleep in the Scriptures will awaken a new understanding of sleep and sleeplessness in our lives. May God use his easy-to-read, scientifically and biblically informed common sense approach to help lead us to rest.

Kevin Paszalek
Professor
Vice Principal for Administration
Moffat Bible College
Kijabe, Kenya
AIM International

Many books have been written about the physiologic and psychological aspects of sleep, but Surrendered Sleep: A Biblical Perspective *by Charles W. Page, M.D., is a cutting edge and comprehensive book about the spiritual aspects of this often ignored one third of our lives—our sleep. It addresses the impact that sleep has on our daily lives … all from a biblical perspective. I was fascinated with how much has been said about sleep by the ultimate sleep doctor—God himself.*

Dr. Page's book addresses how to achieve peaceful sleep through a restructured and vibrant relationship with God. This is quite a gift as approximately half of our population suffers from insomnia.

I find this book to be authentic, factual, and instrumental in supplying the missing link in the current literature on sleep … that is, the spiritual component.

I highly recommend this book to all who desire to improve the peacefulness of their sleep and the quality of their lives. This is how it was meant to be from the beginning of time according to the One who never sleeps, the One who watches over us during our days and our nights.

Ronald Cates, M.D.
Fellow, American Academy of Sleep Medicine

TABLE OF CONTENTS

INTRODUCTION 4

CHAPTER ONE: THE LORD OF SLEEP 8

CHAPTER TWO: A CALM HEART: Introduction 20

CHAPTER THREE: A CALM HEART: Trust in God 26

CHAPTER FOUR: A CALM HEART: A Process of Belief 36

CHAPTER FIVE: A WISE HEART: Priorities 56

CHAPTER SIX: A WISE HEART: Daily Pursuit of God 68

CHAPTER SEVEN: A WISE HEART: Relationships 76

CHAPTER EIGHT: A WISE HEART: Work 82

CHAPTER NINE: A WISE HEART: Financial Choices 90

CHAPTER TEN: A WISE HEART: Physical Activity and Diet 100

CHAPTER ELEVEN: A WISE HEART: A Proactive Approach to Health 106

CHAPTER TWELVE: A RESPONSIVE HEART 118

CHAPTER THIRTEEN: A DISOBEDIENT HEART 132

CHAPTER FOURTEEN: A SERVANT'S HEART 146

CHAPTER FIFTEEN: A SEPARATED HEART 154

CHAPTER SIXTEEN: AN ENDURING HEART 164

CHAPTER SEVENTEEN: BALIN JAM! 180

APPENDIX "A": ENDNOTES 182

SLEEP DIARY 191

FOREWORD

Have you ever really been excited about something on the horizon of your life? Something that you have seen develop from infancy stages? Something that very few know is coming? Something that you believe will have a dramatic impact? When Chuck released the final manuscript of this brilliant work, I read it with great anticipation. After reading three prior editing versions of the manuscript, I could see what was coming. I have over 7000 volumes of books in my personal library and as a senior pastor, I spend countless hours at bookstore shelves. There is not another work in the world like *Surrendered Sleep*.

When one thinks that almost one third of our lives will be spent sleeping, it makes sense that we know much about the subject. Our lives are incredibly steeped in searching for answers in those awake and active hours, yet so little is invested in the pursuit of honest treatment for rest and sleep. The key to this book is the recognition that each of us must personally unlock the secret of surrendering every aspect of sleep.

What Dr. Page does so well in this book is to take the reader down a determined and disciplined path, one that allows him to understand and experience transforming rest and sleep. The combined perspective of God's Word and medicine provides a unique approach to sleep issues. Written from Chuck's "real life" perspective, these insights are both practical and profitable for the person who wants to sleep well.

I am honored to help introduce Dr. Page and his tremendous work *Surrendered Sleep: A Biblical Perspective* to you. Both have been appointed for this generation. Chuck has done his homework. If you do yours, your sleep will be transformed.

Michael M. Cook
Senior Pastor
Albuquerque's First Baptist Church

INTRODUCTION

Got sleep? This question is permeating our modern culture. Gone are the days of "early to bed—early to rise." Our nanosecond culture now interprets being "healthy, wealthy, and wise" as processing volumes of information rapidly and multitasking numerous activities at an overwhelming pace. As a consequence we are sleeping less than previous generations—and are beginning to experience its ill effects.

This question has given birth to multiple other questions in our pursuit of sleep. If sleep is an issue, then how can refreshing sleep be acquired? Is sleep medicine the answer to identify an underlying sleep disorder? Should herbal remedies, such as valerian root, be used to induce a good night's sleep? Are sleeping pills the answer for insomnia? Can the answer be found in spirituality, new age religion, or cognitive behavioral therapy?

To make sense of the multiple sleep options presented to us, we must first step back and ask a more fundamental question. Got God? Tackling this question will help us gain insight into the issues behind our sleep problems, which in turn will give us perspective on our questions regarding sleep. Only through a relationship with the One who created sleep can we understand how to evaluate these options.

Has it ever crossed your mind that God is interested in your attitude towards sleep? God desires surrender in every aspect of our lives—

including our sleep. Although this concept of surrender may be an unpopular one in our culture, this is certain—we will surrender our lives to something. We can choose to yield our lives over to the things that rob us of sleep such as fear, pride, guilt, bitterness, or despair, or we can choose to submit to the Lord of sleep. *Surrendered Sleep: A Biblical Perspective* explores the ways we can yield our hearts to God and experience His grace, love, and freedom as we lay our heads down for rest.

On a personal level, sleep has been elusive. As a surgeon, nights are rare when my sleep is not disturbed. In addition to the middle-of-the-night phone calls and trips to the emergency room that hinder my ability to rest, I also suffer with obstructive sleep apnea. In my quest for sleep, I found volumes of sleep literature dealing with the medical aspect of insomnia, but little biblical instruction about sleep issues. I am keenly aware of those areas where I fail to apply all of the principles discussed in this book. Our challenge—both author and reader—is to strive together towards the high calling for which God has already taken hold of us (Philippians 3:12). May we both grow as we surrender to His will for our lives.

The purpose of this book is not to undermine modern sleep medicine, but rather explore sleep from a biblical perspective. We must learn to respond to God in the midst of our sleep issues and not miss the big picture of God's intervention in our lives. Let me emphasize that this book does not guarantee you a good night's sleep or introduce you to a magical formula for sleep. *Surrendered Sleep: A Biblical Perspective* encourages you to recognize how the One who never slumbers or sleeps is working in your life and how to know Him better.

Chuck Page M.D.
www.SurrenderedSleep.com

CHAPTER 1
THE LORD OF SLEEP

Don't you agree then, that the Christian gospel should have something to say about the sleeping third of our lives as well as the waking two-thirds of it?

~John Baille, Scottish theologian~

People will do just about anything to get a good night's sleep. Michael Jackson, the "King of Pop", died receiving propofol injections for his chronic insomnia and sleep issues. Jackson, paying *$150,000 a month* for these services, called this white liquid anesthetic his bedtime "milk". His desperate quest for sleep and the extreme remedies he pursued are, on a broader scale, a reflection of the widespread condition in our culture. Michael Jackson's story is an unfortunate illustration of the despair that many people experience in their search for sleep. In fact, this pursuit of sleep is the new craze.

Almost everywhere in the media one finds a new "cure" or "breakthrough" to help get a little shuteye. More self-help books and insomnia websites are appearing every day. A new medical specialty, sleep medicine, has evolved as we learn more about the science behind sleep. For instance, we've learned about the harmful side effects of sleep deprivation which include weight gain, increased risk of heart disease, poor work performance, traffic accidents, memory loss, and impaired thinking.

Vince reached up and slapped himself on the cheek— hard. His eyes felt gritty and the center line of the road was wavering from side to side. He reached over and turned the radio up and switched channels. Maybe some really horrible music would keep him awake long enough to make it home. He only had a couple more miles. The cup of coffee in the cup holder was cold, but he swallowed the bitter brew anyway. Maybe there would be enough caffeine in it to keep him awake until he reached his house.

Vince glanced at the in-dash clock as he pulled into the driveway—2:30 a.m. He was going to have to cut down on the overtime. He was exhausted. He couldn't wait to collapse into bed.

What seemed like moments later, his eyes sprung open. He rolled over and groaned, looking at the clock—4 a.m. He tried to drift off to sleep again, but each time he started nodding, he jerked back awake. An hour later he gave up, walking unsteadily into the kitchen where he started making himself a strong—very strong—pot of coffee.

It was going to be another one of those days.

Poor sleep is at epidemic levels. Over sixty million Americans

How many times a week do you experience episodes of restless sleep or insomnia?

_____

What are your coping mechanisms for staying awake during the day?

_____

_____

_____

_____

_____

What spiritual issues are you wrestling with that could be causing you to lose sleep?

suffer from insomnia and lack of sleep. A conservative study notes that about thirty percent of Americans experience insomnia at some point in their lives. Women are twice as likely as men to experience sleep deprivation, and those who live in the southern and midwestern portions of the United States report the most interruptions in sleep. Similarly, the 2009 National Sleep Foundation's *Sleep in America*™ poll shows that problems with sleep are on the rise.

What is worrisome is that the studies show that Americans are coping with these problems in an unproductive manner. These methods include using caffeine to stay awake (40%); eating foods high in sugar or carbohydrates (19%); using tobacco (18%); using prescription or over-the-counter drugs to keep them alert (11%); and just accepting it and going on (62%).[1]

Christians are not immune to sleep issues. A recent study revealed that seventy percent of all evangelical Christians put getting a good night's sleep as one of their top priorities. "When born-again adults are compared with those who are not born again, the only two differences are that the born-again contingent is more interested in participating in the faith-related opportunities, and they are more interested in getting a good night's sleep." [2]

The evangelical world has been relatively silent in presenting a biblical perspective on the topic of sleep. For example, when was the last time you heard a sermon about sleep or read a Christian book about sleep? More than likely, you never have.

As we explore the scriptures, we will begin to understand that not only does God have a lot to say about sleep, it was all His idea! In contrast, volumes of sleep literature that have been written from a psychological, medical, or humanistic perspective have nothing to say about the spiritual aspect of our sleep issues. In fact, medicine has yet to understand why sleep is such a necessity for the human race. Scientifically, our understanding of sleep is still clouded in mystery. Again, this is not to discredit modern sleep medicine, but we may be searching for answers to our problems of insomnia and poor sleep in the wrong places. Modern science overlooks the fact that our ability to sleep is based not only on the physical dimension, but on the spiritual dimension as well.

SLEEP THEOLOGY

Unlike His Creation, the omnipresent God who spoke the universe into being exists outside of time. God eternally existed prior to the creation of the day and night order and will continue to exist eternally after that order has passed.[3] Consequently, God is not confined by the need or desire to sleep. The psalmist declares, "He will not let your foot slip—he who watches over you will not slumber; indeed, he who watches over Israel will neither slumber nor sleep. The Lord watches over you—the Lord is your shade at your right hand; the sun will not harm you by day, nor the moon by night." [4] Unlike mankind, God's eyes never close.

What does the reassurance that God is watching over you twenty-four hours a day mean to you?

_____

_____

_____

_____

_____

The word "shade" comes from the Hebrew word tsel *which means "defense." What things do you need God to defend you from?*

_____

_____

_____

_____

_____

Take the time to write out a prayer right now, asking God to be your defense in those struggles you face.

_____

_____

_____

_____

_____

_____

_____

_____

_____

_____

_____

_____

David was aware of God's activity in the still of the night: "Though you probe my heart and examine me at night, though you test me, you will find nothing…" [5] He discerns God's existence outside of the day/night constraints which so defines us as human beings: "If I say, 'Surely the darkness will hide me and the light become night around me,' even the darkness will not be dark to you; the night will shine like the day, for darkness is as light to you." [6] What we fail to recognize is that God is just as active while we sleep as when we're awake. He doesn't sit idle, He's not dormant, and He's very interested in our lives even while we sleep. Our God is a twenty-four/seven God. He works around the clock. From God's perspective, there is no difference between the daytime and the nighttime.

God, who breathed life into man, also created in mankind the physiological, emotional, and spiritual need for sleep. God created man to live within the confining cycle of night and day, to exist within the constraints of the creation order. He could just as well have created us without the need for sleep, or created our sleep requirements to equal other animals that He made. For example, elephants, donkeys, roe deer, horses and giraffes routinely sleep less than three hours a day. [7] He didn't though. He uniquely designed us to spend almost one-third of our lives slumbering.

Christians understand easily that God is intimately involved in our wakeful hours because we are consciously aware of His presence. We believe that He leads, guides, and directs us.

12

We incorrectly assume, however, that as we transition into sleep, God somehow shifts into neutral, too. Our mindset towards God in the twilight hours is typically "Goodnight, God. See you in the morning," as if He idly waits for us to wake up to begin anew.

In fact, in direct contrast to our understanding of the day and night sequence, God's schedule seems to be quite the opposite. For instance, God's daily creative work that we see in the beginning of Genesis actually started fresh as the sun went down. "And God saw the light, that it was good; and God divided the light from the darkness. God called the light Day, and the darkness he called Night. *So the evening and the morning were the first day.*" [8]

During each subsequent day of creation, the scriptures repeat the same sequence again and again—"the evening and the morning…" In fact, the Hebrew calendar follows this same pattern. In the Jewish tradition, the day begins and ends as the sun goes down. Likewise, we see God beginning each new day of creation as the sun goes down. Just as our God formed and filled our world through the nighttime hours and continued that work as the sun rose again, so does our unchangeable God continue His creative work in our lives during the stillness of the night as we lay down to sleep. Even in our sleeplessness, He is creatively working out His wonderful purpose in our lives.

Even the heavens communicate God's unending Presence. "The heavens declare the glory of God; and the firmament shows His handiwork. Day unto day utters speech, and night unto night reveals knowledge." [9] God gave mankind a reminder of this aspect of His nature when He created the stars. Although the stars are not always visible and are hidden from view, we know that they are there. God, like the stars He created, is always present. This celestial example challenges us to become more aware of His presence and activity in our lives—especially as we lay down to sleep. We need to remember that, when our minds shift into neutral on our beds, God continues to work.

The Bible is saturated with examples of God's activity toward mankind during sleep. When God saw Adam was alone, He put him in a deep sleep and made his soul mate, Eve. [11] While Abraham slept, God established his covenant of love with him, assuring him of long life and legions of descendents. [12] As Jacob slept on a rock for a pillow, the Lord assured him of fathering a blessed nation that would inhabit the land where he was sleeping. [13] As Egypt slept, the Lord passed over, rendering judgment to the Egyptians and deliverance to the nation of Israel. [14] As Israel slept in the wilderness, God protected them by a wall of fire by night. As Israel slept, every night God provided them manna from heaven.

As Gideon slept, God confirmed His will through a fleece. [15] As Boaz slept, God was not only providing him a wife of great character, but was working out His plan of redemption for mankind. [16] As a fugitive from his son, Absalom, David

14

slept, confessing: "I lie down and sleep; I wake again, because the Lord sustains me." [17] Running in despair for his life, Elijah slept under a juniper tree while the angel of the Lord ministered to his physical needs. [18]

While Hezekiah and all of Jerusalem slept under siege and imminent destruction, the Lord intervened and slew the Assyrian army. [19] While Elisha slept in peace, an unseen army of angels was gathering at night to defeat the Syrians who were secretly preparing to take the city of Dothan and capture the prophet. [20] While Jeremiah slept, he received God's vision of Israel's restoration and confessed: "At this I awoke and looked around. My sleep had been pleasant to me." [21] While most of Judea slept, God chose to announce His incarnation to lowly shepherds declaring the birth of His Son. [22]

Consistently throughout the scriptures, God, in a variety of ways, is seen moving, working, interacting and communing with people during their sleeping—or sleepless—hours. God, who is the same yesterday, today, and forever, has not changed His strategy.

God is the Lord of Sleep. He is not some mythical sandman who drops by and dishes out a comfortable good night's rest, and He's certainly not bound by any protocol or routine that we have set up in our attempts to sleep. His agenda for our lives has always been to draw us closer to Himself and spread His name throughout our world. God may very well

Romans 10:17 states "Faith comes by hearing, and hearing by the Word of God." We acquire more faith and trust when we read His Word. How is your faith strengthened when you read the accounts of all the ways that God has intervened and ministered in the lives of saints and sinners alike?

_____

_____

_____

_____

_____

_____

_____

_____

be using our sleep issues to fulfill His purpose for our lives. Therefore, God's perspective and agenda regarding sleep may be very different from our own. We must reject the idea that because we know God, we are entitled to a good night's sleep. God looks at sleep, as well as every aspect of our lives, as avenues to know and serve Him better.

THE GIVER OF SLEEP

God, in His wisdom, did not add an eleventh commandment, "Thou shalt sleep eight hours each night." The Bible is silent on how much sleep we need. The Bible assumes that when we are tired, we will eventually sleep. God knows the framework of each individual and their own physiologic need for sleep. The scripture says that sleep is not a right or an entitlement, but a gift from God: "It is vain for you to rise up early, to sit up late, to eat the bread of sorrows; for *so He gives His beloved sleep.*" [23]

Sleep can sometimes be elusive. The harder we try to nod off, the harder it becomes to rest. Sleep, from God's perspective, is not something that we should strive to attain. Like salvation, it is a gift. A gift must be received in faith with a thankful heart. Our priority in receiving this gift of sleep is positioning our hearts with the proper attitude.

The Giver of Sleep knows every detail about our lives. The One "who brings out the starry host one by one, and calls them each by name," has also numbered each individual hair on our scalp. He knows our past, our present, and our future. He knows our weaknesses, our strengths, and our aspirations. The Giver of Sleep also knows what is most appropriate for us at any given time. Sometimes God in His sovereignty gives us sleep. Our response should be thankfulness. Sometimes in His goodness He keeps our eyelids open, preparing us for something or revealing Himself to us in a deeper way.

Have you ever had the experience of giving your children a gift only to have them become spoiled or lack any appreciation for the gift? Similarly, God knows when it is appropriate to give the gift of sleep to His children. [24] He always has His best in store for us. "Don't be deceived, my dear brother. Every good and perfect gift is from above, coming down from the Father of the heavenly lights, who does not change like shifting shadows." [25]

God is not selfish or stingy when it comes to giving us sleep. He loves us so much that He came to die for us so that we could have a vibrant relationship with Him both now and in eternity. "What then, shall we say in response to this? If God is for us, who can be against us? He who did not spare his own Son, but gave him up for us all—h*ow will he not also, along with him, graciously give us all things?*" [26] Again the psalmist notes: "No good thing will He withhold from those who walk uprightly." [27]

More than a new pill or a new insomnia self-help book, we must not only get to know the Giver of Sleep, but we must search our attitudes in regard to sleep. Our greatest need is

Are there areas in your life that you have refused to surrender to God? Listen to what God says to Jeremiah in Jeremiah 29:11: "'For I know the plans I have for you,' declares the LORD, 'plans to prosper you and not to harm you, plans to give you hope and a future.'" Are you afraid of what God would ask of you if you surrendered these areas of your life to Him?

not for better, more productive rest, but to know the Lord of Sleep. Consequently, as we learn to surrender our lives to this Lord of Sleep, we may learn to sleep better.

SLEEP PROBLEMS: SYMPTOMS OF HEART ATTITUDES?

Behavioral psychology suggests that the way to battle sleeplessness is to change the way we think about sleep. Cognitive behavioral therapy aims at replacing negative thoughts and habits about sleep with more positive ones. This technique has been shown to be more effective than sleeping pills in helping improve long-term sleep in those suffering with insomnia. Although sleep talk and CBT are beneficial and have their place in treating insomnia, one could potentially miss out on the larger picture of God's purpose for sleeplessness. These techniques may help you sleep, but you may miss out on God. The Bible presents a different perspective about human nature and sleep. The Bible addresses mankind's heart.

The Bible declares that a change in behavior is not enough. Mankind needs more than just a tune-up or a superficial change in the way we think. Man needs an internal change of heart that ultimately manifests itself in our behavior. True change comes from a transformation of the heart. God looks beyond our behavior into underlying motives: "For the Lord does not see as man sees; for man looks at the outward appearance, but the Lord looks at the heart." [28] Solomon admonishes "above all else, guard your heart, for it is the wellspring of life." [29]

What complicates the issue is that on our own, our hearts can be a challenge to understand. "The heart is deceitful above all things, and desperately wicked; who can know it? I, the Lord, search the heart, I test the mind, even to give every man according to his ways, according to the fruit of his doings." [30] Not only does God search our hearts, He desires to illuminate our minds and give us understanding through scripture. By exposing our hearts to the truth of God's Word, an internal transformation can begin. "For the word of God is living and powerful, and sharper than any two-edged sword, piercing even to the division of the soul and spirit, and of joints and marrow, *and is a discerner of the thoughts and intents of the heart.*" [31]

Just as shortness of breath, or neck and jaw pain can be the symptoms of an underlying cardiac condition, issues with sleep can be an outward manifestation of an underlying spiritual attitude. Has it ever crossed your mind that your sleeplessness may be the result of an underlying attitude? God's Word is the most effective diagnostic tool that we have to help diagnose and treat those spiritual issues that manifest themselves as we lay down to sleep. As we explore the scriptures, different patterns of spiritual attitudes toward sleep begin to emerge.

Have you been diligent in guarding your heart, setting it apart to God? Write down some of the things you have or have not done in surrendering your heart entirely to God.

_____
_____
_____
_____
_____
_____
_____
_____
_____
_____
_____
_____

CHAPTER 2
A CALM HEART:
INTRODUCTION

"I will lie down and sleep in peace, for you alone, O Lord, make me dwell in safety." (Psalm 4:8) The word "peace" in the above passage is shalom *in the Hebrew. This word encompasses more than just feelings of security. It pertains to our safety, health, and welfare as well. The word "safety" is* betach *in the Hebrew, and it means assurance and confidence. Here God is telling us that we will lie down in sweet peace as it pertains to our health and well-being, and that we can do so with confidence and assurance.*

The last thing my parents would say after I was tucked into bed was "Good night, sleep tight. Don't let the bedbugs bite!" I developed a childhood paranoia about bed bugs creeping out of the darkness and into my covers. As I grew up, I noticed that the bed bugs never materialized, and blew them off as another bedtime joke from my parents. However, bedbugs are real! We're seeing a resurgence of them in our society due to weaker pesticides and the increase in world traffic. They are more than a medieval myth. We read in the news about finding bed bugs in dirty New York hotels, dorm rooms, and various other places.

Bed bugs, or *cimex lectularius,* burrow into one's skin, feeding on the blood, sucking it out of the body much like little vampires. We're also experiencing a spiritual epidemic of "bed bugs," little critters that are sucking the life out of so many of us. Insomnia affects over 60 million Americans today, and the majority of cases are caused by these spiritual bed bugs—worry, bitterness, fear, and regret among other things. The only way to battle these spiritual bugs is with a spiritual pesticide—faith.

Unfortunately, there are no formulas on how to grow faith strong enough to defeat these life-sucking pests that rob us of our rest. Physically, we condition our heart with stress to increase our cardiac output, our endurance. One does not just go out and run a marathon without training and conditioning the heart to endure the stress that long-distance running requires. Getting our heart into spiritual shape also involves a process of conditioning. As we exercise our faith in times of stress, our heart is strengthened to endure the storms that potentially rob us of sleep.

A calm heart is one that has been conditioned to sleep well because of the progressive assurance of God's provision and protection in every detail of life. One of the best examples of this conditioning of the heart can be seen in the life of Peter.

It was about this time that King Herod arrested some who belonged to the church, intending to persecute them. He had James, the brother of John, put to death with the sword. When he saw that this pleased the Jews, he proceeded to seize Peter also. This happened during the Feast of Unleavened Bread. After arresting him, he put him in prison, handing him over to be guarded by four squads of four soldiers each. Herod intended to bring him out for public trial after the Passover. So Peter was kept in prison, but the church was earnestly praying to God for him. The night before Herod was to bring him to trial, Peter was sleeping between two soldiers, bound with two chains, while sentries stood guard at the entrance. Suddenly an angel of the Lord appeared and a light

Do you find yourself in a situation that could be compared to Peter's on an emotional level— surrounded all around by spiritual enemies, chained by circumstances? How do you respond to these stresses?

_____

_____

_____

_____

_____

_____

_____

_____

_____

_____

_____

_____

_____

shone in the cell. He struck Peter on the side and woke him up. "Quick, get up!" he said, and the chains fell off Peter's wrists. [1]

Peter had been jailed many times in the past, but this time the situation was different. Peter was alone, chained, and surrounded by four squads of soldiers awaiting the ending of Passover. Herod, who had just executed James, planned a rigged trial followed by Peter's execution.

We would expect the apostle Peter to at least be reminiscing over his life or possibly pining over regrets, perhaps even praying for deliverance. Ironically, we see the disciple dozing. There is no evidence of any anxiety over his present imprisonment, any regret over his past, or any fear of his future trial and imminent execution. How could Peter show this kind of equanimity and peace during this time of turmoil in his life?

Approximately fifteen years had passed since the resurrection of the Lord. Peter, through God's process of conditioning, had come full circle. From sleeping carelessly at the Garden of Gethsemane the night before the crucifixion, to now sleeping in the full assurance of faith, Peter could confess: "Cast all of your anxiety on Him because he cares for you."[2] Perhaps, during this trial, Peter reflected back to an experience in a storm time when he believed that Jesus did not care about his circumstances.

That day when evening came, he said to his disciples, "Let us go over to the other side." Leaving the crowd behind, they took him along, just as he was, in the boat. There were also other boats with him. A furious squall came up, and the waves broke over the boat, so that it was nearly swamped. Jesus was in the stern, sleeping on a cushion. The disciples woke him and said to him, "Teacher, don't you care if we drown?" He got up, rebuked the wind and said to the waves, "Quiet! Be still!" Then the wind died down and it was completely calm. He said to his disciples, "Why are you so afraid? Do you still have no faith?" They were terrified and asked each other, "Who is this? Even the wind and the waves obey him!" ³

After an exhausting day of ministry, Jesus urges His disciples to leave the crowd behind and travel with Him in a boat to the other side of the Sea of Galilee. Jesus, tired from the day's work, fell asleep in the bow of the boat. Being seasoned fishermen, the disciples were accustomed to unexpected storms that arose on the Sea of Galilee. But as this storm grew in intensity, so did the fear in the disciples' hearts.

Exasperated and exhausted by their own efforts, they remembered the presence of the Lord in the boat. The Savior was calmly sleeping after a rigorous day of ministry, free from worry. Being the omniscient Lord, He knew the storm was coming, but He was able to totally trust the Father's plan for His life as well as the provision for His safety.

Can you think back to a time when you were sure God didn't care about your circumstances, but He intervened despite your doubts? How does knowing God has been faithful in the past help you to have faith in the present?

What circumstances contribute to the increasing fear or anxiety that may be keeping you awake?

_____

_____

_____

_____

_____

_____

_____

_____

_____

_____

_____

"Teacher, don't you care if we drown?" the disciples asked anxiously. Jesus, the Master of the seas, quieted the storm with a simple vocal command, and then turned and rebuked His disciples for their lack of faith. After all of the ministry and all of the teaching of the Lord, they still had much to learn.

Yes, Peter had come a long way in his walk with the Lord since that encounter with an angry tumult on the Sea of Galilee. He had seen Jesus' example of "grace under pressure" and how the Lord was able to sleep amidst great adversity. He had also endured many experiences in his journey of faith that helped to condition his heart to rest in the Lord and sleep soundly. This was part of God's great work in his life manifesting itself in his sleep habits.

How does this transformation into a calm heart work out into our lives? How can we have this calm heart to sleep soundly? The answer is in developing what I call faith sleep. One aspect of "living by faith" involves learning to "sleep by faith". There are many aspects of our lives that can run well without faith—even sleep. But the one thing we cannot do without faith is please God. "And without faith it is impossible to please God, because anyone who comes to him must believe that he exists and that he rewards those who earnestly seek him." [4]

As Christians, our desire should be to have every aspect of our lives—even sleep—be pleasing to the One whose eyes never close in slumber. Therefore we must learn to sleep by faith. Faith sleep involves knowing some things and then doing some things. We'll discuss these in the next few chapters.

How often are you tempted to anger towards God because you don't feel that He cares whether you're drowning in your circumstances or not? Again, look to the past when He's been faithful. How does this help in reining in the doubt and anger?

_____

_____

_____

_____

_____

_____

_____

_____

_____

_____

25

Do you believe, at a deep-down gut level, that God is in control of your life and that He is with you through everything? Why or why not?

CHAPTER 3
A CALM HEART:
TRUST IN GOD

As children, we all had fears of monsters crouching in the closet ready to pounce on us if we dared to shut our eyes. As we grew in knowledge, we learned that many of those fears were mere figments of our imagination. We understood that fear of a one-eyed purple people-eater lurking under our bed was only contrived in our heads. Spiritually, as we grow in faith, and we understand God's providence, protection, and provision in our lives, our fears begin to fade in the light of His presence. "When I was a child, I spoke as a child, I understood as a child, I thought as a child; but when I became a man, I put away childish things." [1] Our fears, however real they may be, require us to take on Christ's perspective.

Peter's ability to sleep in faith may have been encouraged by witnessing Jesus' demonstration of peaceful sleep amidst the storms of life. Not only does Jesus provide the power to calm these internal storms, He also provided the example that evening 2,000 years ago. The Savior who slept through the squall modeled calm sleep during adversity. Jesus lived His whole life free of anxiety, guilt, fear, or dread. His example is a model of total faith, total trust, and unrestrained abiding in God the Father. We must learn to follow the example of Jesus and Peter, learning complete trust in the One who never grows tired or weary. In order to do so, there are several things we must know in our hearts and commit to do them.

I. Trusting in God's providence as we sleep

Whatever the circumstances we face that tempt us to worry instead of sleep, we must first learn that these circumstances are according to God's plan and purpose for our lives. Like the disciples in the tumultuous sea, or Peter chained in between Herod's guards, we must understand that God is orchestrating everything in our lives for His purposes. We have to recognize that nothing can happen to us except what God allows and wills in our lives.

Romans 8:28 says this: "We *know* in all things God works for the good of those who love Him, who have been called according to his purpose." [emphasis the author's] First, this verse states that we know—not think, understand, or feel. The Greek word for "know" in this passage is *eidon*. It literally means to perceive with the senses, to inspect, to examine, and to experience. This means we should be able to look at past events where God has been faithful, to perceive that in our present circumstances, He will be faithful as well.

There are times we may not be able to rationalize or understand the circumstances we encounter. This verse does not mean that "all things" are necessarily pleasant for us. On the contrary, sometimes things we experience in life can be

Have you ever thought about the trials Jesus went through? Here was God Himself, in the flesh, putting Himself at the mercy of the humanity He had created. How does reflecting on His experiences help you to view yours in a different light?

27

Our God never, not for one moment, loses sight of us or where we're at. One effective way of building faith, is to "pray God's Word." It reaffirms for us the promises that He has made, and it opens spiritual doors of opportunity for God to work miraculously in our lives. An example of praying God's Word using Psalm 121 is found on the next page.

quite painful. We must also <u>know</u> that God not only plans things for us to strengthen our faith, He takes the choices we make and the consequences we endure and uses these experiences as well for our benefit or "good". There are no situations we find ourselves in that happen without the knowledge and direction of a loving God.

This verse reminds us as believers that God does things for us, <u>not</u> to us. Like the drowning disciples, our human nature cries out with questions. "God, do you really care about my circumstances?" "Don't you care that I am drowning in debt, or tragedy, or illness?"

We must also come to know that God has only good intentions for our lives. Jeremiah 29:11 says: "'For I know the plans I have for you,' declares the Lord, 'plans to prosper you and not to harm you, plans to give you a hope and a future.'" This was given to the nation of Israel during a time of crisis, but I believe it is relevant for us personally today. Like Peter, we will learn to cast all our cares upon Him, "for he cares for you." [2] By faith, we must come to know that nothing is allowed in our lives except that it is filtered through the loving sovereign hands of the Lord.

II. Trusting in God's protection as we sleep

As the waves began to fill the boat, the disciples began to fear for their very lives. Jesus was there in the boat, protecting them just as He promised them when He said, "Let us go over to the other side." [3] By His very words, Jesus was promising them that they would arrive at their destination.

Psalm 121 reassures us that God is constantly protecting us.

> I lift up my eyes to the hills—where does my help come from? My help comes from the Lord, the Maker of heaven and earth. He will not let your foot slip— he who watches over you will not slumber; indeed, he who watches over Israel will neither slumber nor sleep. The Lord watches over you—the Lord is your shade at your right hand; the sun will not harm you by day, nor the moon by night. The Lord will keep you from all harm—he will watch over your life; the Lord will watch over your coming and going both now and forevermore.

This psalm reminds us repeatedly that the Lord is watching or "keeping" us. This means that He guards, protects, and cares for us, and we can rest in this knowledge. God is always watching us as we sleep keeping us from all harm, even as He watches our coming and going, not allowing our foot to slip.

The life of Elisha gives us another example of how God protects us while we are sleeping. Because of Elisha's ability to predict every move of the Arameans, the King of Aram sneaks an army into Samaria to capture the prophet.

Father God, there have been many times in my life when You have held me up and have kept me from falling. Your Word tells me that You do not slumber or sleep, not for one moment, and that I am always before You. It tells me that You watch over my life. Well, my life is kind of ragged right now, God; I really need Your strength and Your presence to comfort me. You are the maker of all heaven and earth, and I know that there is nothing that You cannot do. Father, I believe. Help me with my unbelief. Strengthen my faith. Show me the way. In the name of Your precious Son, I pray. Amen.

Then he sent horses and chariots and a strong force there. They went by night and surrounded the city. When the servant of the man of God got up and went out early the next morning, an army with horses and chariots had surrounded the city. "Oh, my lord, what shall we do?" the servant asked. "Don't be afraid," the prophet answered. "Those who are with us are more than those who are with them." And Elisha prayed, "O LORD, open his eyes so he may see." Then the LORD opened the servant's eyes, and he looked and saw the hills full of horses and chariots of fire all around Elisha. As the enemy came down toward him, Elisha prayed to the LORD, 'Strike these people with blindness." So he struck them with blindness, as Elisha had asked. Elisha told them "This is not the road and this is not the city. Follow me, and I will lead you to the man you are looking for."And he led them to Samaria. [4]

An unrecognized and unexpected danger was developing around the city of Dothan as Elisha and his servant slept. What the servant saw was the great peril of the conquering army which had surrounded them. But Elisha, looking through the eyes of faith, saw God's army of angels surrounding the city protecting its inhabitants. Like Elisha, we need to learn to see fearful situations through the eyes of faith.

So it is for us. We can rest with the assurance that God is

surrounding us with His hedge of protection, even when we are unaware of the potential danger. Like Elisha, we must know in our hearts that "those that are with us are more than those who are with them." Our fears diminish when we understand that God's army of angels keeps us secure as we sleep. "You will not fear terror of the night nor the arrow that flies by day. For he will command his angels concerning you to guard you in all your ways." [5]

David also comprehended God's watchful, protective eyes over him as he slept. Hiding in the desert from his son Absalom who was seeking to kill him, David confessed in his evening prayer: "I will lie down and sleep in peace, for you alone, O Lord, make me dwell in safety." [6] Rising in the morning, David again thanks God for keeping him free from harm during the night: "I lie down and sleep; I wake again, because the Lord sustains me. I will not fear the tens of thousands drawn up against me on every side." [7] David, Peter, and Elisha all learned that the secret to sleeping calmly amidst adversity was trusting in God's ability to shield them from the enemies during the night watches.

III. Trusting in God's provision while we sleep

Many times, the greatest hurdle to going to sleep is all of the things yet to be done. The things that didn't get checked off our "to do" list weigh heavily on our minds as we lay our heads on our pillow. We need to learn how to leave our unfinished tasks with God, resting in His ability to pick up where we left off if He desires to do so. (On the other hand, we sometimes put things into our daytime agenda that shouldn't be on our "to do" list in the first place.)

Psalm 127:1-2 states: "Unless the Lord builds the house, its builders labor in vain. Unless the Lord watches over the city, the watchmen stand guard in vain. In vain you rise early and stay up late, toiling for food to eat—for he grants sleep to those he loves." This passage reminds us of the futility and frustration of a busy lifestyle that follows our own agenda. Our ambitious agenda may impress others, but from a heavenly perspective, you may be spinning your wheels. Another aspect of this psalm that we have not discussed is the understanding that God is providing for our needs even as we sleep if we are obeying His will for our lives on a daily basis. Being still and trusting God typically defies our logic and reasoning. Like drowning in quicksand, we think that trying harder to get out will help. However, our pointless struggling only serves to suck us down deeper in the mire. We must learn to relax and allow God to deliver us.

This lesson had to be learned the hard way for the nation of Israel after the Lord miraculously brought them through the Red Sea. As they slept in the desert, the Lord provided yet another miracle in the form of manna to eat every morning. This provision was always just enough to get them through the day—no more, no less. If they hoarded more than they needed, it would rot and stink to high heaven. The nation learned to trust in the Lord one day at a time; anything else

What unfinished business at the end of the day plagues your sleep at night?

_____

_____

_____

_____

_____

_____

_____

_____

_____

_____

_____

_____

was only an act of futility. For forty years, God fed over one million people in a desert that had no food or water in sight. He is that same God today. We must simply learn to trust in His provision as we travel through our own personal wilderness experiences.

There's the story of the mother who was talking to her pre-school daughter at bedtime.

"Mommy, is the moon God's light?" the little girl asked.

"Yes, sweetheart," the mother replied.

"Will God ever put out His light, mommy?"

"No, God never goes to sleep," the mother answered.

With simple childlike faith, the little girl told her mother, "Well, as long as God is awake, there is no sense in both of us staying awake." And off to sleep she went.

A calm heart is one who understands that God never slumbers or sleeps, and in simple childlike faith, rests peacefully. A calm heart understands God's promise of providence, protection, provision, and presence as he or she drifts into slumber. Like a child, allow yourself to be enveloped in the arms of the Omnipresent One.

Fall to sleep in His arms.

CHAPTER 4
A CALM HEART:
A PROCESS OF BELIEF

How do we nourish a calm heart when the "bed bugs" of our lives begin to pester us as we lay down to sleep? There are no magical formulas or protocols. Maturing in this area involves a process of trusting and obeying God in the midnight hours. The problems that race through our minds and rob us of sleep can be defeated if we learn to take steps of faith. One example of this process in the midnight hours was demonstrated in a Philippian prison.

> Then the multitude rose up together against them; and the magistrates tore off their clothes and commanded them to be beaten with rods. And when they had laid many stripes on them, they threw them into prison, commanding the jailer to keep them securely. Having received such a charge he put them into the inner prison and fastened their feet in the stocks. But at midnight Paul and Silas were praying and singing hymns to God, and the prisoners were listening to them. Suddenly there was a great earthquake, so that the foundations of the prison were shaken; and immediately all the doors were opened and everyone's chains were loosed. [1]

PROBLEMS AND OUR PRISON

Imagine how bleak the picture looked that night for Paul and Silas. Bruised and beaten, lying in a foreign country chained to the ground, their ministry in Philippi appeared to have come to a standstill. The imprisoned disciples were faced with multiple problems. In pain, Paul and Silas cried out to God, and tremendous power was released. Miraculously, the prison doors were opened and the chains fell off their feet and God was glorified.

Sometimes the storms in our lives arise unexpectedly out of nowhere. Other times, the problems we face seem to be ones of a more chronic nature that slowly wear down our defenses. Whether we are blameless or responsible for our problems, we are promised that they will come. These trials can potentially imprison us in the bondage of fear—especially as we lay down to sleep. Like Paul and Silas in the Philippian jail, we must first learn to adjust our perspective and see our problems through the lens of faith.

A CHANGE IN PERSPECTIVE

We must learn to see our problems as opportunities. First, our trials present us with the opportunity of personal growth. "And not only that, but we also glory in tribulations, knowing that tribulation produces perseverance; and perseverance, character; and character hope." [2] James puts it this way: "My brethren, count it all joy when you fall into various trials, knowing that the testing of your faith produces patience. But let patience have its perfect work, that you may be perfect and complete, lacking nothing." [3] Even when we are responsible for our troubles we can still use our failures as a platform for growth. "Now no chastening seems to be joyful

What chains and prison bars encircle you? What things in your life, whether people, circumstances, or habits, hold you in bondage?

_____

_____

_____

_____

_____

_____

_____

_____

_____

_____

35

for the present, but painful; nevertheless, afterward it yields the peaceable fruit of righteousness to those who have been trained by it." [4] Even when we sin, our loving God can take our failures and use them to mold our character. Confessing to Him our failures and moving on in faith is the first step in this process of transformation.

Secondly, we must understand that God can use our circumstances as an opportunity to influence others. There is no question that an entire "multitude" was watching Paul and Silas as they were beaten unjustly in Philippi that day. Subsequently, that evening the prisoners were still listening intently to them as they approached God in praise and prayer.

Being aware that others are watching our response in difficult times should not only change our attitude but also our actions. Observe what the disciples abstain from in this circumstance. There's no hint of them complaining, grumbling, or questioning as they are beaten and thrown into the inner prison under false pretenses. Although they could have demanded a trial prior to their beating and imprisonment, they chose to be silent before their accusers.

When we realize that God may be using our problems to draw others to Himself, we begin to see our circumstances through a different set of lenses. We will begin to ask God to use our problems to bring others to a deeper understanding of God and His purposes in their lives.

We must also learn to see our problems through a perspective of neutrality. We must get our hearts into a position ready to trust and obey God, regardless of the outcome. We've already learned about trusting God's activity in our lives as we sleep. His providence is working; His protection is shielding; His provision is supplying. As we yield ourselves to His higher ways, our focus will move away from worrying about the outcome and move toward the character of God Himself. Understanding that our heavenly Father knows best, our desires will be transposed away from our selfish desires and onto what He desires for our lives. Whether God chooses to deliver us from our problems or if He chooses another course—it's all controlled by a sovereign, all powerful, all knowing, all loving Lord.

How do we progress to this perspective that leads to a calm heart? How can this transformation help us as we lay down to sleep? We must saturate our minds with God's Word. When we learn to apply and meditate upon God's Word in the nighttime hours, our hearts will be transformed into ones that are calm and full of peace.

TRANSFORMING OUR PERSPECTIVE THROUGH MEDITATION

Probably the first thing that pops into your mind when you think of meditation is having to sit in the lotus position and chant the same word over and over again. In eastern religions, the idea is to empty your mind and consciousness, but Christian meditation encourages us to fill our minds and focus on God's Word and His attributes. The Bible encourages meditation—especially in the nighttime hours.

> But his delight is in the law of the Lord, and on his law he meditates day and night. [5]

> In your anger do not sin; when you are on your beds, search your hearts and be silent. [6]

> On my bed I remember you; I think of you through the watches of the night. [7]

> My eyes stay open through the watches of the night, that I may meditate on your promises. [8]

Richard J. Foster, in his book, *Celebration of Discipline*, tells us that meditation for the Christian is simply the ability to hear God's voice and to obey His Word. Meditation is a time of fellowship with the Creator of the universe. It's a time to replace the negative emotions we have (fear, anger, loneliness, etc.) with thoughts about God, His blessings in our lives, and the promises He has made to us. Sleep psychologists call this "cognitive restructuring." Amazing, isn't it? Science is just now catching up to what the Bible has been telling us for generations.

From a spiritual perspective, the content of what we fill our minds with is of utmost importance. Let's look at Paul's admonition about meditation in Philippians 4:8: "Finally, my brothers, whatever is true, whatever is noble, whatever is right, whatever is pure, whatever is lovely, whatever is admirable—if anything is excellent or praiseworthy—think about such things."

Our hearts and minds are not a vacuum. Think about the mind as a container of thoughts. In order to remove thoughts out of our minds, we must displace them with something else. Experiment with this: try not to think about green eggs and ham. In trying to push green eggs and ham out of you mind, it boomerangs back into your consciousness. You have to not only push green eggs and ham out of your mind, but replace it with something else.

Here's another example: try to think about going to sleep. See what I mean? If we give a burden to God which is hindering our sleep, there must be a substitute to take its place, or else the very thing we're trying to forget will only return to our thoughts. Prayer is the process where we give all our anxious thoughts to God, knowing He is willing and able to take care of it. Meditation is the process of filling our minds and hearts with things that are noble, right, pure, lovely, admirable, and excellent.

Many pastors tell us that if we can worry, then we can meditate. How is that possible? First of all, what is worry? Worry is meditating on fears. If we can meditate on fears, then we can turn our focus around and meditate on God's Word. Switch your thoughts from worries to Bible verses, and you will find you have less time or inclination to worry.

What types of things do you think about? Do any of these things take away from your time with God? Do they take away from the joy you have with God? What's keeping you from replacing these thoughts and contemplations with uplifting, God-inspired reflections?

_____
_____
_____
_____
_____
_____
_____
_____
_____
_____
_____

Standing on the promises that cannot fail,
When the howling storms of life and doubt assail,
By the living Word of God I shall prevail,
Standing on the promises of God.

("Standing on the Promises of God" by Russell K. Carter, 1886)

TRANSFORMING OUR PERSPECTIVE THROUGH APPLYING GOD'S PROMISES

Whatever we find our need to be at the moment with our sleep issues, whatever trial we may be enduring or circumstances we may be encountering, God's Word has an answer. We can rest in the assurance that all His promises are true! A good idea is have a Bible promise book or reference close to our bedsides to use when insomnia attacks. Here are some examples of promises that we can stand on, promises that encourage us to sit back and trust God.

PEACE	*Peace I leave with you; my peace I give you. I do not give to you as the world gives. Do not let your hearts be troubled and do not be afraid. (John 14:27)*
	You will keep in perfect peace him whose mind is steadfast, because he trusts in you. (Isaiah 26:3)
FEAR	*The Lord is my light and my salvation—whom shall I fear? The Lord is the stronghold of my life—of whom shall I be afraid? (Psalm 27:1)*
	Fear not, for I have redeemed you; I have summoned you by name; you are mine. When you pass through the waters, I will be with you; and when you pass through the rivers, they will not sweep over you. (Isaiah 43:1-2)
DIRECTION	*Whether you turn to the right or to the left, your ears will hear a voice behind you, saying, "This is the way; walk in it." (Isaiah 30:21)*

JOY	*Weeping may endure for a night, but joy comes in the morning. (Psalm 30:5)*
	In Your presence is fullness of joy; at your right hand are pleasures forevermore. (Psalm 16:11)

As we learn to shift our perspective off of ourselves and onto God's plan for our lives, we will be elevated into an attitude of praise and prayer.

AN ATTITUDE OF PRAISE

How often do we remember to cry out in song to God while suffering on our beds? The God who "inhabits the praises of His people" will intervene in our difficulties and circumstances. Typically, we think of praise as a result or consequence of worship. On the contrary, the scriptures suggest the reverse process. Praise is a vehicle that we can use to bring us into the presence of God. "But Thou art holy, O Thou that inhabitest the praises of Israel." [9]

Praise is a verb. It is an activity that can bring us into the presence of God as we lay our head on our pillow. Praise occurs when we commend, applause or magnify God for His attributes. It is an expression of worship and focusing our attention towards God. Praise is a declaration of faith exclaiming that God is with us and in control of our problems. Praise is a sacrificial offering to God. "Through Him then, let us continually offer up a sacrifice of praise to God, that is, the fruit of lips that give thanks to His name." [10] Praise is an action that we must learn to practice

What Bible verses do you use to help you stand on the promises of God? Name one verse that has particularly helped you to weather the storms of life.

What worship and praise songs seem to help you quiet your soul? How does focusing on God in praise help you to cope with your circumstances?

continually—especially when the bed bugs come out from hiding.

> I will bless the LORD at all times; His praise shall continually be in my mouth. [11]

> Rejoice in the Lord always, and again I say rejoice. [12]

> Rejoice always; pray without ceasing; in everything give thanks; for this is God's will for you in Christ Jesus. [13]

One specific form of praise is singing. One of God's most powerful gifts for the sleepless is a song in the night. Paul and Silas experienced this power firsthand after being beaten and placed in the Philippians' jail.

"But no one says, 'Where is God my Maker, who gives songs in the night?'" [14] Instead of seeking our Maker to calm our mind, we strive to deal with hindrances to sleep through our own sufficiency and power. We fail to recognize that God in His grace provides songs in the night to calm the storms in our life. None can say it more eloquently than Charles Haddon Spurgeon did over one hundred years ago in Southwark, England in 1898:

> The great cause of Christian's distress, the reason of the depths of sorrow into which many believers are plunged, is simply this—that while they are looking about, on the right hand and on the left, to see how they may escape their troubles, they forget to look to the hills from whence all real help cometh. They do not say; "Where is God my Maker, who giveth

songs in the night?" .... Night is the season of terror and alarm to most men. Yet even night hath its songs .... And many a night we do have—nights of sorrow, nights of persecution, nights of doubt, nights of bewilderment, nights of anxiety, nights of oppression, nights of ignorance—nights of all kinds which press upon our spirits and terrify our souls. But blessed be God, the Christian man can say, "My God giveth me songs in the night."

Psalm 149:5 admonishes us to worship during the twilight hours. "Let the saints rejoice in this honor and sing for joy on their beds." Notice that we are encouraged to sing for, or to obtain, joy. Joy becomes a byproduct of our singing to the Lord at night. Joy leads us into God's presence. [15] Agreeing with the psalmist, we can say:

By day the Lord directs his love, at night His song is with me—a prayer to the God of my life. [16]

My soul will be satisfied as with the richest of foods; with singing lips my mouth will praise You. On my bed I remember You; I think of You through the watches of the night. Because You are my help, I sing in the shadow of Your wings. [17]

AN ATTITUDE OF PRAYER

A church sign I recently passed had the following posted:

Do you take time out of your day to specifically talk with God about what's going on with your life? Or do you just throw a "hail Mary" pass at God as you're running to your next engagement? Look at your schedule; where can you carve out some one-on-one time with God?

_____

_____

_____

_____

_____

_____

_____

_____

_____

_____

_____

_____

"Instead of counting sheep, try talking to the Shepherd." Now that's great advice! A recent sleep study reveals that "sleep talk" (or cognitive behavioral therapy) has been shown to be more effective than sleeping pills in inducing a good night's sleep. Sleep talk is where you go to a sleep psychologist for sessions to discuss and change your sleep habits.

But believers have a wonderful advantage! We know the One who created us! Who better to talk to than the "original manufacturer"? We have the blessing of being able to sleep talk twenty-four/seven with the Shepherd of Sleep, the One who uniquely created us and fully understands all the problems we are experiencing. Prayer is another means by which we can enter into God's presence. "Let us therefore come boldly to the throne of grace, that we may obtain mercy and find grace to help in the time of need." [18] The apostle Paul says it this way: "Do not be anxious about anything, but in everything, by prayer and petition, with thanksgiving, present your requests to God. And the peace of God, which transcends all understanding, will guard your hearts and your minds in Christ Jesus." [19]

As believers, we must learn to channel all our concerns to God in prayer. Failure to do so is disobedience, a reflection of our desire to handle things in our own wisdom, strength, and abilities. We must learn to let go of the issues of our day and rest in the arms of God. As we transfer our needs, concerns and circumstances over into God's hand a miracle happens—a peace which defies all logical explanation will overwhelm our hearts.

Notice that God promises peace, not deliverance. We are encouraged to present our requests (not demands) to God and leave the outcome up to His will for our lives. God in His providence will either deliver us or give us the grace to endure the circumstances. Understanding that God chooses the outcome does not mean that we are not to pray for deliverance from the storms that we face.

Has it ever crossed your mind that you may be having sleep issues because you have not approached God with your problems? Have you asked for insight into why you're having trouble falling asleep or problems waking up at night? Have you asked Him for help? Many times we "have not because we ask not."

> This is the confidence we have in approaching God: that if we ask anything according to his will, he hears us. And if we know that he hears us—whatever we ask—we know that we have what we asked of him. [20]

God always answers prayer. Sometimes the answer is: "No, I love you too much." Sometimes the answer is: "Yes, but wait." And sometimes the answer is: "Yes and here's more—I thought you'd never ask."

We must first learn to let go of all our concerns at bedtime and put them into the hands of the all knowing, all

Have you ever experienced a time when, exhausted with all your struggling, you just had to let go and allow God to take control?

_____

_____

_____

_____

_____

_____

_____

_____

_____

_____

_____

powerful, all loving LORD.

EXPERIENCING GOD'S PRESENCE

Nurturing an attitude of praise and prayer in the midnight hours elevates us into the presence of God. Before Jesus physically departed planet Earth, He promised His followers that they would never be alone. He prayed the night prior to His crucifixion: "I have given them the glory that you gave me, that they may be one as we are one: I in them and you in me." [21] Experiencing this mystery of the indwelling presence of God, the apostle Paul declared: "I have been crucified with Christ and I no longer live, but Christ lives in me." [22] What did Jesus mean when He promised to be with us? Oftentimes we fail to grasp the fundamental importance of the presence of God to us as believers, and we fail to understand the practical application of practicing that presence and reality of God in our daily lives.

The first key to recognizing the presence of God is to understand that God already abides within hearts of believers. Unlike the disciples who experienced the external presence of God during a squall on the sea, those who have received Christ have the indwelling of the Holy Spirit. All the necessary resources for a calm heart are already possessed for those who are in Christ. There's no need for another experience, self-help book, or another conference. For the believer, the power within us provides all the necessary resources.

As believers, we have the power of Christ living within us. The same one that spoke "Peace, be still," can also calm the anxious storm in our hearts at bedtime. A. W. Tozer, in *The Knowledge of the Holy*, declared: "The healing balm distilled from the garments of the enfolding Presence cures our ill before they become fatal. The knowledge that we are never alone calms the troubled sea of our lives and speaks peace to our souls. That God is here, both scripture and reason declare. It remains only for us to learn to realize this in conscious experience."

Secondly, we can learn from the disciples that we can call on Jesus for help, and He will respond. So many times we try to solve our problems on our own, through our own efforts, and end up sinking deeper in desperation. When situations come that rob us of our sleep, we need to recognize His presence, and in faith, call on God's name. The disciples learned this lesson the hard way. After exhausting all other means to save themselves in the storm, they remembered the One sleeping at the front of the boat. That night on the turbulent waters, they learned that Jesus was all that was needed.

Recently, I was reminded of how God's presence works in and through our lives. Jonathan, our second-born son, never learned to ride a bicycle. After several skinned knees and hurt feelings while riding with training wheels, Jonathan fearfully abandoned any further attempts to ride a bike on his own. We tried every strategy known to mankind to help

Are you ever aware of the presence of God in your daily walk? Do you quiet yourself so that you can hear His voice? Do you slow down to seek His counsel? How can you cultivate these habits so that you are aware of God working in and through you?

our son overcome his fear of bicycles. We bathed him in encouragement—which ultimately failed. We modeled how to ride a bike. We pushed him around on his bike over the soft grass, holding both him and his bicycle up, hoping to prevent any falls. Still his fear of failure (and falling) was too much to overcome. Ultimately his dad (me) tried a little "tough love" on him. "Son, you are gonna learn to ride this bike—if it's the last thing I do." That was a disastrous approach that totally backfired. Jonathan was more terrified of me than his bicycle. What made the situation more embarrassing was that our two younger daughters were both riding by the age of five. Jonathan, now almost ten years old, was still paralyzed when it came to putting his feet on the pedals.

Fortunately, my wise, insightful wife came up with a brilliant idea—a bicycle built for two. At first Jonboy was terrified to get on the back seat—especially after those horrific bicycle experiences with his father (me). The first twenty minutes or so were overwhelming for my son. But all of a sudden, something on the inside clicked. My son realized how liberating riding a bicycle could be when he rode in tandem with his father. After ten years of fear, Jonathan realized what he had been missing all along. Now Jonathan begs me daily to go with him on excursions on our bicycle built for two. Jonathan has learned some great lessons, but Dad has learned an even greater lesson.

When our heavenly Father promised to be "with us," He

did not intend to give us a set of training wheels and let us go out on our own. He plans include more than going with us part of the way, holding us up, and catching us before we fall and skin our knees. He definitely had more in mind than just encouraging us or giving a good dose of "tough love". God desires to come along and ride the journey with us—together—kind of like that bicycle built for two. Living with His indwelling presence involves getting on board with God, letting Him guide, direct and steer our lives. We only have to trust and peddle as hard as we can. God wants to be with us on the journey, not just watch our attempts to do it on our own. Many Christians live their whole lives trying to peddle and steer their lives on their own, thinking that God is blessed by simply watching us go down the road of life on our own. Others quit after several failures of trying it on their own, wounded from scars of discouragement.

The person on the back seat in a bicycle built for two is called the "stoker." The stoker's main task is to pedal and stay in submission to the driver in the front. The driver's role is to steer, brake, change gears, and speed up and slow down. Get the picture? When we allow the indwelling Holy Spirit to be the driver of our lives, and we perform our task as a submissive stoker, nothing can take us down.

How does practicing the presence of God help us as we lay down to sleep? He doesn't just give us the principles of providence, protection, and provision as we sleep and then let us take life out for a ride ourselves. He's there inside

Be Thou my vision, O Lord of My heart; Naught be all else to me, save that Thou art.
Thou my best thought, by day or by night,
Waking or sleeping, Thy presence my light.

("Be Thou My Vision" by Dallan Forgaill, 8th century)

49

us—teaching, comforting, and guiding. That's the role of the Holy Spirit in our lives. He wants us to get on board with Him, and He'll show us the way. It's more than being reactive when the storms of life catch us by surprise—its twenty-four/seven riding with Him.

DISPLAYING GOD'S POWER

Christ's power will materialize in our lives as a natural consequence of experiencing God's presence. As the disciples called on the presence of Christ in the boat, He miraculously calmed the tempest that threatened their lives. As Paul and Silas prayed and sang in the presence of the Lord that night, God brought an earthquake to free them of their chains of bondage. Paul prayed for this experience for the Ephesian church, that they would understand "what is the exceeding greatness of His power toward us who believe, according to the working of His mighty power." [23] He also prayed that God would powerfully enable them: "Now to Him who is able to do exceedingly abundantly above all that we ask or think, according to the power that works in us, be glory in the church by Christ Jesus to all generations, forever and ever." [24]

As with the disciples in the storm, and Paul and Silas in the Philippian jail, God's power may be demonstrated in us by delivering us from our problems. God, in His sovereign power, can move mountains. At other times, God's power will be demonstrated in giving us the ability to endure the storms and trials that we encounter. There were many times that Paul was imprisoned without God's deliverance. In fact, during those times of incarceration, Paul was empowered to write his prison epistles, which have blessed and encouraged generations of believers. Think of what you would have missed out on if Paul had been delivered from prison every time—the blessing of hearing and reading about "His mighty power that works in us." [25]

There's no doubt about it—God is working out His purposes in our lives through trials, storms and problems. First, we must adjust our thinking and see our problems through an eternal perspective. Renewal of our minds will lead us to respond in praise and prayer to our loving Father. An attitude of praise and prayer will help us recognize the power of God's presence in our lives. By following God through this process, His power will unshackle the chains that imprison us in our sleeplessness. The Holy Spirit will begin a work of calmness and peace that will ward off any "bedbugs" that try to torment our hearts.

CHAPTER 5
A WISE HEART:
PRIORITIES

See then that you walk circumspectly, not as fools but as wise, redeeming the time, because the days are evil. Therefore do not be unwise, but understand what the will of the Lord is.
(Ephesians 5:16-17 NKJV)

Our nanosecond culture has embraced what I call the "Hanna Montana syndrome." Hanna lives out the "best of both worlds" mentality for us on her Disney show. She sings about enjoying all the glitz of being a rock star icon while simultaneously experiencing the freedom of being an anonymous teenager.

The more we watch the sitcom, the more we realize that having the "best of both worlds" is only a fantasy contrived by Disney. Hanna is constantly faced with the cold reality that she can't be both famous and anonymous at the same time. If we're not careful, we can slip into this "best of both worlds" mentality with our sleep life. Like Hanna Montana, we have the illusion that we can live in one world, one way, during the daytime, and a completely different world in the twilight hours. We cannot live independently of God's principles during the day and then expect God's blessings when we sleep.

Janelle groaned. She had been up since 5 a.m., running from one event to another. It had been soccer practice for Madelaine, baseball practice for Joseph, and the cook-out at the Jones', Daniel's new boss at work. She still had two loads of laundry to get finished before church tomorrow...that is if she didn't want her family to go naked.

When she finally went to bed at two that morning, her hand hesitated above the alarm clock. There wasn't any pressing reason for them to be at church, she reasoned to herself. It wouldn't hurt to skip one morning, she thought, refusing to acknowledge that skipping church was now becoming a habit. She pushed the clock away and laid down, tossing and turning the rest of the night.

A wise heart understands that the best strategy for a good night's sleep begins the moment one wakes up. Our choices, our pursuits, our thoughts, our handling of relationships, and the people we encounter—all these and more help to determine the quality of our sleep. Throughout the next chapters, we're going to study the make-up of a wise heart and the different issues we face, one at a time.

First, a wise heart understands the interdependence of the spiritual, physical, and emotional decisions we make and how these choices affect the quality of our sleep. Proverbs 23:19 tells us, "Listen, my son, and be wise, and keep your heart on the right path." The instructions for how we're to live are clearly laid out in the Bible. If the Bible is

Most of us live quite busy lives. Looking at the schedule you now have, where do you think you can carve out time to read the Bible and find the answers for the things you're struggling with?

_____

_____

_____

_____

_____

_____

_____

_____

_____

_____

_____

_____

_____

our instruction manual for life, it really makes sense to sit down and read it if we're struggling physically, mentally, or spiritually.

Many times we fail to recognize that the daily pursuits in our lives, and the choices we make, may very well be linked to the thoughts and worries that keep us awake. An old adage says, "A clean conscience makes a soft pillow." In following God's path of wisdom, we learn contentment. When we live our lives under the instruction of God, we know that we're living in His will. A wise heart chooses a lifestyle that is conducive to sleep.

The scriptures encourage us to take heart issues very seriously. Our hearts control the actions, thoughts, and responses that flow from every decision we make in our lives. Let's look at Proverbs 4:23 (KJV) again. "Keep thy heart with all diligence; for out of it are the issues of life."

The word "keep" here comes from the Hebrew *natsar*, which means to protect and to maintain. "Diligence" (the Hebrew word *mishmar*) means to literally imprison or put in jail. What God is telling us is to wrap our hearts up tightly, to protect them against anything that comes against them that is contrary to what He teaches us, to literally imprison them in His Word!

What are these issues of life? The Hebrew word *chai* that the word "life" comes from means everything from our appetites, the community of people we live in, to our sustenance. Everything that we face on a daily basis is a heart issue. And as we have seen, the only way to keep our hearts, and therefore our lives, on the right path, is to immerse them in God's Word.

Although more intricate and complex, our hearts are very similar to our personal computers. We can install almost any type of software into our computer to perform a desired task. The function and the ability of our computer is determined by the software that we program it with. Likewise, God's Word can be used to do the same thing. For example, Proverbs chapter three focuses on the blessings we receive when our hearts are transformed by wisdom. The writer is encouraging us to "program" wisdom into our hearts.

> My son, do not forget my teaching, but keep my commands in your heart, for they will prolong your life many years and bring you prosperity. Let love and faithfulness never leave you; bind them around your neck, write them on the table of your heart. Then you will win favor and a good name in the sight of God and man. Trust in the Lord with all your heart and lean not on your own understanding; in all your ways acknowledge him, and he will make your paths straight. [1]

We must learn to internalize principles and habits that will lead us to wise choices and ultimately a wise heart. Walking

After reading Proverbs 3:1-6, what "software" is God instructing us to program into our hearts in this passage?

_____

_____

_____

_____

_____

_____

_____

_____

_____

What is the blessing regarding sleep that is in the Proverbs 3:21-24 passage?

_____

_____

_____

_____

_____

_____

_____

through life with a wise heart enables us to avoid many of the obstacles and difficulties that others may experience. This concept overflows into getting a good night's rest. Good daytime choices position us for a good night's sleep by giving us contentment and a clean conscience before God.

> My son, preserve sound judgment and discernment, do not let them out of your sight; they will be life for you, an ornament to grace your neck. Then you will go on your way in safety, and your foot will not stumble; when you lie down, you will not be afraid; when you lie down, your sleep will be sweet. [2]

It's funny how God uses the most ordinary of circumstances and activities to speak to us. I had one of these experiences the other night when I opened the door to my refrigerator to stuff in some more leftovers. It's bizarre (but true!)— God spoke to me while I was packing more stuff into my overcrowded refrigerator.

When you have a large growing family, you need a BIG refrigerator—especially if there are boys involved. (Have you seen what they can eat? It's mind-boggling!) Well, as our family grew, my wife began to grumble about the lack of space in the old icebox. We tried to cram in so much into that smaller fridge that some of it was left to turn into unidentifiable "stuff" because it was pushed to the back and forgotten. We eventually bought a new refrigerator, doubling our available space. However, I predicted that our new fridge would quickly become stuffed to the gills again with food we'd forget about and never eat.

We finally came to realize that our refrigerator would never be big enough. The problem was not the size of the refrigerator. The problem was with our priorities. First, we weren't eating everything, and second, we were just piling newer stuff on top of old, allowing three-week old leftovers to rot and mold in the back where no one ever looked. We had to do some serious reassessing of our needs and what would be put in the refrigerator. Things aren't perfect, but the fridge sure does smell better!

So what did God say to me while I was standing there in front of an open refrigerator, trying to find one more empty space to stuff full of leftovers? He told me that our lives were pretty much like my overburdened refrigerator, and we were only designed to fit in a certain amount of activities a day. He told me we needed to learn what to save and what to throw away, and if we didn't, then our lives would begin to "stink" with the rot of overcrowded expectations and commitments.

Unlike the message our society of "abundant living" puts out there, we don't need to overcrowd our lives with insignificant things that are not necessary, things that do nothing to further God's purposes in our lives. Having more time is not the answer. Time is not the problem—our prioritizing (or the lack of it!) is the problem.

What is your process for judging and discerning? Is it a haphazard, "fly by the seat of your pants" process, or is it a methodical and logically reasoned out course of action? What steps can you take to make your decisions well-thought out and in line with God's Word?

————————

————————

————————

————————

————————

————————

————————

————————

————————

————————

————————

————————

When we prioritize one thing—our relationship with Jesus Christ—everything else will fall into place. Our spiritual "refrigerators" and our physical lives will become more organized with a sweeter smell. We must learn that "priorities" have to become a priority in our lives!

One of the many by-products of God's prescribed course of wisdom is that of "sweet" or pleasant sleep. Sweetness is the most pleasurable sensation known to man. When we approve of something, we describe it as "sweet." Sweet sleep is what we all desire—the ability to wake up refreshed, energized, and ready to take on our daily tasks after a night of tranquil rest.

This promise of "sweet sleep" is a conditional one based on preserving sound judgment and discernment. Webster's defines "judgment" as the process of forming an opinion or evaluation by comparison. Similarly, "discernment" is defined as the power to see what is not evident to the average mind; the power to distinguish and select what is excellent.

Sound judgment and discernment begins with making decisions based on God's standard and will for our lives. Internalizing this process of good judgment and discernment will help us have pleasant or sweet sleep. A practical reminder for us in our daily activities is to remember the "sleep test."

Just what is this "sleep test"? Well, you've probably heard someone mention the following phrase, or something close to it: "I'll be able to sleep well tonight because…", and will be referencing a decision that was made well. This is the sleep test, and a good rule for us to adopt as we go about our day.

Will I be able to sleep well if I make this financial decision? If I treat this person in this manner, will it allow me to sleep at night with a clear conscience?

In medical training we learned to apply the sleep test to clinical decisions with our patients. *If I do this operation on this patient, will I be able to sleep tonight?* We always wanted to make a clinical decision that would give us a clean conscience knowing we had done what we felt was the best and safest treatment for our patient.

In life decisions, big and small, wisdom encourages us to always ask these questions:

- Will this choice help me sleep sweetly tonight and for the rest of my life with a clean conscience before God and man?

- Will this decision lead me down a path of regret and anxiety as I lay my head down on my pillow?

But what if we're at a place where we don't know how to decide? The answer is as close as your Bible: "If any of you lacks wisdom, he should ask God, who gives generously to

Can you name a time when a decision you made left you restless and unable to sleep? How about a time when a decision left you sleeping easy?

_____

_____

_____

_____

_____

_____

_____

_____

_____

_____

_____

all without finding fault." [3] God really wants what is best for us. He desires to give us the wisdom that we need to make choices that will honor Him. If you're having trouble with a decision, ask God. He will show you what you need to do. He will help you make wise choices that will lead to a wise lifestyle which will predispose you to sweet sleep.

Sometimes we experience poor sleep because of poor lifestyle choices. A wise heart understands that there is an intricate balance between the spiritual, the physical, and the emotional, and that they all contribute to a healthy sleep. A wise heart must choose a proactive lifestyle during the daytime that will position him or her for a good night's sleep. A wise heart sleeps sweetly because he or she has made wise choices.

There are several steps to making wise decisions and choices that lead to well-rested bodies. Learning to prioritize is the first step. Let's face it—there are so many things on our to-do lists, all calling for our attention...and our undivided attention at that! Many difficulties with sleep could be easily prevented if we would plan wisely and establish God's priorities for our lives.

Distinguishing what is good from what is best is another aspect of "preserving good judgment and discernment." Our culture presents us with a multiplicity of options that may cloud choosing God's best for our lives. Learning to say "no" to lesser things frees us up for time to choose what is God's best for us. As we make God and spiritual items first priority, lesser things seem to fall into place.

Jesus loved parables, so let's use one here. Packing a minivan for summer vacation can be a chore, especially with five kids, two dogs, one cat, and a lizard. Everyone has their idea of what is important to pack for the trip. The kids' perspective on what is necessary for the journey is radically different from what mom and dad thinks is important. (Fortunately, decisions in our family are not based on the democratic process!)

I've learned to pack the big stuff first, and then fit most of the little things into the cracks. On our spiritual journey, we must learn to prioritize the big stuff first. Subsequently, most of the little stuff will fit into the cracks of our lives.

"Trust in the Lord with all your heart and lean not on your own understanding; in all your ways acknowledge him, and he will make your paths straight." [4] The New International Version also includes this footnote about the last portion of this quote...or "and he will direct your paths." When we acknowledge God concerning the priorities of our lives, it means not only that we agree with him, but we intend to follow his direction. Subsequently, God will not only direct our choices, but will straighten the paths that lie before us.

Priorities are a necessity. We only have a limited amount of time each day and the way we use our God-given time

What are the big things or priorities in your life? What should be the most important and what should be included as space permits?

_____

_____

_____

_____

_____

_____

_____

_____

_____

_____

_____

_____

reflects what we consider most important. Time well-spent is the time spent with God going over our game plan for the day. When we spend time with God—through reading the Word, writing down what you believe to be God's priorities in your life, and praying—sleep is easier to achieve. However, you can't just be a "hearer of the Word" and not a "doer." Don't just devise a game plan—incorporate it into your life.

Time is a resource that is nonrenewable and nontransferable. You cannot store it up, slow it up, hold it up, divide it up, or give it up. You can't hoard it up or save it for a rainy day—when it's lost, it's unrecoverable. When you kill time, remember, it has no resurrection.
A. W. Tozer

CHAPTER 6
A WISE HEART:
DAILY PURSUIT OF GOD

List the priorities of your life and their order of importance to you. Be honest with yourself and with God.

In the last chapter we talked about priorities, of aligning ourselves with God's will. In organizing our priorities, how do we determine the importance of each aspect of our lives? Perhaps the first order of our priorities is found in Matthew 6:33: "But seek first his Kingdom and his righteousness, and all these things will be given to you as well."

The key for the believer is to understand that everything flows out of our relationship with God. We develop good judgment and discernment in our relationships, our work, our finances, and our health as we connect to the resources we have when we are in fellowship with Christ. Only as we become more intimately involved with God and get our direction from Him can we develop God-pleasing priorities.

The question in the sidebar about listing your priorities is not meant to induce or paralyze you with guilt. The last thing you need when you're trying to get a good night's sleep is something else to beat yourself over the head with. It's important to realize that we will never measure up to God's high call and standard this side of heaven. What's important to remember is that the journey (intimacy with God) is as equally important as the destination (heaven).

The purpose of life is a relationship with God. We grow in every area of our lives as we daily cultivate this relationship. A.W. Tozer calls it "the pursuit of God." In his preface to his book of the same title, Tozer says: "It is a solemn thing, and no small scandal in the Kingdom, to see God's children starving while actually seated at the table … For it is not mere words that nourish the soul, but God Himself, and unless and until the hearers find God in personal experience, they are not the better for having heard the truth."

Do you hunger for God with an insatiable appetite? Do you find yourself with deep longing and almost painful expectation looking forward to your time with God? Don't feel like you're alone—many do not. But the wonderful thing about life is the ability to change direction at any time, to commit to a course of action, to search hungrily for the God who loves us above all else. And as the Bible tells us in Jeremiah 29:13: "You will seek me and find me when you seek me with all your heart."

An example of the type of relationship we should strive for with God can be found in King David. David was described as "a man *after* God's own heart." The scriptures could have used other prepositions to describe their relationship. For example, David could have been called "a man *with* God's own heart;" "*of* God's own heart;" "*for* God's own heart;" or "*from* God's own heart." History could remember him as the one "*near* God's own heart." Instead, God skillfully chose the word "after" to convey the desire of David's heart—of following hard towards something (or in this case, *Someone*) in a purposeful direction.

As we examine David's "wilderness" experience, we begin to understand why he was called one "*after* God's own heart." After forty years as king, David was running again—this time from his own son, Absalom. Absalom started a coup to overthrow David and establish himself as Israel's king. David's enemies were in hot pursuit of him as he hid out in the desert (II Samuel 16-18). Far from his palace comforts in Jerusalem, David struggled to survive. It was during this time that he composed several of his fugitive psalms, ones that liken his pursuit of God to his enemies' pursuit of him (Psalms 3,4, and 63). We get a glimpse of his pursuit of God and how it relates to his sleep in the wilderness experience.

Listen to the heart of David in Psalm 63:

> O God, You are my God;
>   Early will I seek You;
>   My soul thirsts for You;
>   My flesh longs for You
>   In a dry and thirsty land
>   Where there is no water.
>
> So I have looked for You in the sanctuary,
>   To see Your power and Your glory.

Because Your lovingkindness is better than life,
My lips shall praise You.
Thus I will bless You while I live;
I will lift up my hands in Your name.
My soul shall be satisfied as with marrow and fatness,
And my mouth shall praise You with joyful lips.

When I remember You on my bed,
I meditate on You in the night watches.
Because You have been my help,
Therefore in the shadow of Your wings I will rejoice.
My soul follows close behind You;
Your right hand upholds me. [1]

In this psalm, David shows us that his passion for God trumps his desire for sleep. His thirst for God wakes him up early in the morning. As David lies down to sleep, he joyfully remembers and meditates on God. This preoccupation with God is echoed in David's evening prayer in Psalm 4:4: "Be angry and do not sin. Meditate within your heart on your bed, and be still."

In prior chapters we have discussed the art of meditation, praise and trusting God for protection. For now the point is that David's continual focus—morning, noon, and night—was his pursuit of an all-consuming God. David refused to allow anything to get in his way of his pursuit of God—even sleep. If David was given sleep, he would praise God for

How would you define your relationship with God? A stranger? A casual acquaintance? A friend? A father?

His protection (Psalm 4:8). If David was unable to rest, he would joyfully focus his thoughts on the One whose "love is better than life."

Ironically, the harder David was pursued by his enemies, the harder David pursued intimacy with God. He confesses: "My soul follows close behind you." (Psalm 63:8) This is what it means to be "*after* God's own heart." David's experience gives us a glimpse of how our desire to experience God should master all other desires.

Christians today have almost forgotten that God is a Person. He's not some amorphous being "out there," merely looking down and long-distance handling the affairs of creation. And because he is a Person, we cannot hope at all to fully know Him just by reading His Word or participating in church programs. We must actively seek conversation, intimacy, and knowledge of Him just as we would any friendship we try to cultivate among people we know.

Do you ever think of God as someone who thinks, feels, enjoys, laughs, cries, loves, desires, or suffers? Have you ever thought of where we get these attributes as human beings? Isn't it from the Father that created us in His image? Because we are made in His image, we have the ability to know Him. The only thing that separates us from this knowledge is our sin and the lack of power we have to know Him because of that sin.

But God, in His infinite grace and mercy, provided the solution to that problem as well—through the sacrifice of His Son, Jesus, for the remission of sins. Because of Jesus' sacrifice, God flings the knowledge of our sins as far as the east is from the west and says He remembers them no more. (Psalm 103:12; Jeremiah 31:34)

But how does having or not having a relationship with God affect our sleep? It is said that each of us has a God-shaped hole or vacuum in our hearts that only He can fill. If we are incomplete, if we are not living to our full potential, then our bodies, minds, and spirits are under enormous stress, struggling to reach that potential. We are empty and unfulfilled because the very thing we need to fill us (God) has not been done. We struggle with issues in our lives because the Author of our lives has not been consulted.

It's much like buying a car and then, the moment it breaks down, trying to fix it yourself when you don't have a mechanical bone in your body. You take it to someone who is experienced in automobile repair and take advantage of their expertise to get your car back on the road. Since sleep was God's idea, the most reasonable approach would be to hotly pursue the One who gives us sleep and who understands all the issues you are facing.

Shouldn't we, as Christians, be in pursuit of the expertise of the Creator of all things in finding peace and fulfillment in our lives that allows us to sleep well at night? We live in an

What have you done to try to become intimately involved with God?

_____

_____

_____

_____

_____

_____

_____

_____

_____

_____

_____

Evaluate your schedule. Is everything on your list necessary and expedient, or is just what you choose to do? How do all these activities and pursuits affect your relationship with God?

out-of-balance, stressed out, and exhausted generation. We have voluntarily chosen a lifestyle that cannot be sensibly maintained and wonder why we're worn out and out of touch with our family, our friends, and our God.

We cram our lives with every possible experience without consideration of priorities and boundaries. We're wishy-washy about healthy diets, physical activity, and health maintenance. Our attitudes toward work and rest are out of balance. Relationships with other people are put on the back burner. Our affection and attention has been focused on temporary material things resulting in financial problems. And then when we lay our heads on our pillows, we have no clue as to why we're having trouble sleeping.

A wise heart will grow in the understanding that the best strategy for getting a good night's sleep begins with a comprehensive decision to adjust our lifestyles to biblical principles. And these principles can be condensed into two items:

- Love the Lord your God with all your heart and with all your soul and with all your mind. [2]
- Love your neighbor as yourself. [3]

First and foremost, we must pursue a vibrant, living relationship with our Heavenly Father. We must ask Him for good judgment and discernment regarding all of our decisions.

Secondly, we need to prioritize our relationships from the most important (our immediate family) on down. We can't just tell them we love them; we must show them in action and deed that they are loved. And that doesn't mean time in pursuit of things. It means time in pursuit of knowledge of their hearts, their fears, their desires, and their dreams.

By rightly ordering our lives according to these principles, we will progressively experience the refreshing sweetness of sleep that God's Word promises.

CHAPTER 7
A WISE HEART:
RELATIONSHIPS

If you could only sense how important you are to the lives of those you meet; how important you can be to the people you may never even dream of. There is something of yourself that you leave at every meeting wi
th another person.

- Fred Rogers - The World According to Mister Rogers

Which of your relationships is causing you the most trouble in getting a good night's rest?

A lot of tossing and turning in bed is caused by tension in our relationship with others. Guilt, regret, anger, bitterness, worry, and misunderstanding are all emotions that surface as we lay down to sleep. Difficult relationships are sometimes part of the experience of being broken people in a fallen world. Relational tension with family, co-workers, church members, and neighbors can drain us of our joy and rob us of our sleep.

Steve Arterburn, in his book *Regret-Free Living*, says that we need to periodically stop, step back, and evaluate our relationships. We have to ask God to show us all the things that we are "too small, weak, and purposely busy to grasp ourselves." [1]

For many, it's easier to continue on in a dysfunctional relationship than it is to stop and assess the problems. It's easier to become busier and busier and ignore any potential areas of concern that may be surfacing within a relationship, whether it's a family member, a friend, or someone you work with. It's easier to turn away from glaring signs of trouble in a toxic relationship than it is to confront it.

It's called "denial." And we think if we ignore it, it will go away.

It won't.

Do you realize that God doesn't want these relationships in your life to continue as they have been? Do you know that He wants to help you build vibrant, healthy intimacies and friendships? Do you understand that Jesus came to earth to establish relationships with people, and that as His followers, that is our objective as well?

Usually the difficulties we have with a relationship stem from several things:

- Guilt over the way we've treated someone that manifests as anger towards that person or an inability to be around them;
- Bitterness and anger toward someone over the way they have treated us;
- Blithe disdain for the relationship when we choose other projects or work ahead of the relationship that triggers anger, hurt, and bitterness from the other person;
- A power struggle within the relationship;
- Unresolved conflicts within the relationship.

Which of your relationships needs the most attention? What are your hopes for the future of that relationship?

Thinking of your troubled relationships, which of the reasons listed apply to the difficulties you're experiencing?

_____

_____

_____

_____

_____

_____

_____

_____

_____

_____

_____

_____

Since the beginning of time, man has tried to shift the blame for anything wrong to another person. When God confronted Adam about his eating the forbidden fruit and the knowledge of his nakedness, Adam tried to shift the blame to God and Eve: "The woman whom *You* gave to be with me..." [2] When God confronted Eve, she blamed the snake. Everything was someone or something else's fault (including God's!) but never their own. We've been stuck in this same pattern of passing blame ever since.

Just like a 10-step program, we can't move forward if we don't acknowledge our contribution to any relationship problem. The Word tells us in Proverbs 3:3: "Let not mercy and truth forsake you; bind them around your neck, write them on the tablet of your heart..." As we open God's Word of Truth, we realize how far we have fallen from His standards in how we relate to others. Wisdom encourages us to confess our sin, not only to God, but to the one sinned against as well. We must reconcile the relationship (where appropriate) before we can bring ourselves before God and expect blessing.

Pastor Jerry Cook, in his book *A Few Things I've Learned Since I Knew It All*, describes several particularly poignant ways we treat others inappropriately and thereby harm our relationships. In our task-oriented world that is increasingly devoid of human contact, it's very easy to get into these habits.

He says that one thing we tend to do is see people according to their functions, not their humanity. We see them based on the role they have in our lives. The garbage man is the one who takes out my garbage. The surgeon is the guy who takes out my gallbladder.

We also treat them like objects. In the office they're "employees" or "customers." In medicine we refer to them as "patients" or "hernias" or the "amputation in Room 215." In religious circles we treat people as objects when we refer to them as "decisions" or "souls." We also marginalize people according to politics: conservative, liberal, Democrat, Republican, pro-life, pro-choice. The list is endless.

Jesus did not see people across these lines. They were not functions, objects, symbols, interruptions, or political parties. They were broken humanity with real needs. He wept over them. When we fail to do the same, we break the heart of Jesus.

It's very easy to think that others should give us the benefit of the doubt when it comes to our actions, words, and thoughts. However, we somehow neglect to apply this standard to others we interact with. There has to be a balance of truth, mercy, and forgiveness in our relationships.

Understand there are relationships that are toxic, unhealthy, and abusive. God does not expect us to open ourselves up to these unhealthy relationships again as if nothing ever

Think of all the people you come into contact with on a daily basis. How do you see them? How do you feel about them as people? How do you interact with them? Is this an area you need God to help you with?

_____

_____

_____

_____

_____

_____

_____

_____

_____

_____

_____

_____

Thinking beyond those relationships that cause anger, which ones are just irritating or annoying? By your attitude or unwillingness to set limits, how have you contributed to the annoyance factor in those relationships? What can you do to change that?

_____

_____

_____

_____

_____

_____

_____

_____

_____

_____

_____

_____

_____

happened. But in order to move forward, forgiveness is essential. Anger and bitterness are detrimental and erosive to our physical and spiritual health. Paul's encouragement to the early Ephesian church was this: "In your anger do not sin: do not let the sun go down while you are still angry, and do not give the devil a foothold." [3]

We should make it a habit to deal with our anger before lying down to bed. We need to confront those issues that anger us, praying for God to show us how to handle the situations that are creating the anger and bitterness. If we allow "the sun to go down" and don't deal with internal anger, then it begins to fester like an abscess in our body. Like an abscess, anger unresolved will spread systemically and affect our entire lives—body, mind and spirit. God's prescription for forgiveness and resolving anger issues isn't for the benefit necessarily of those who wronged us, but for ourselves most of all.

The word "anger" used in Ephesians 4:26 comes from the Greek word *parorgismos* which means much more than just anger. It includes wrath, indignation, and exasperation. It's a composite of all those negative feelings that you experience in any irritating circumstance or relationship. Anger is not the only emotion Paul is telling us to deal with. He's telling us to deal with all the issues that negatively impact us on a continuing basis so that none of them gain a foothold on our health, our spirit, or our sleep.

Coming to the end of our day, knowing that we've treated people in a Christ-like way, creates a comfortable pillow to lay our head on. Wherever we are—in public, church, work, the grocery store, or within our families—we should treat people and interact with them in the same manner that Jesus did, in the examples that He left for us to follow. Aligning our relationships aright will go a long way in helping us achieve the peaceful sleep we desire.

CHAPTER 8
A WISE HEART:
WORK

The Toyota automotive company has been under fire recently for the accelerator defect in over 2 million cars that have been recalled. It all began in August 2009 when a family made a frantic 911 call while speeding down a California freeway. The Lexus they were driving could not be controlled because of a stuck accelerator. The car eventually reached a speed of nearly 120 miles per hour and the driver was unable to slow down or turn the car off while it was in gear. The car careened off the road, killing all the passengers. Toyota is in the process of recalling all these cars, and in the interim, recommends its customers slam on the brakes and shift to neutral if their accelerator sticks while driving.

It's been a scary ride for all—especially the Toyota drivers! From another point of view, perhaps we could all benefit from a recall of another sort. I'm talking about our brains, and in particular, our attitudes about work. Folks, our accelerators are stuck in the wide open position. We're out of control and headed for a fatal collision!

As the competition in our work culture increases, corporate loyalty decreases, our work becomes more portable due to new technologies, and we find ourselves racing down the freeway of life overwhelmed by our work. Then we wonder why we have problems slowing down to sleep!

Before we wreck our lives, our relationships, and our health, let's slam on our mental brakes for a minute and put our lives in neutral as we reassess our attitudes about work.

Work is part of God's plan to provide us with spiritual, physical, financial, and mental well-being. Having a balanced and contented work life is one of the greatest challenges we face in modern society. Unfortunately, our culture pressures us to "live to work" instead of "working to live." It's very easy to get our perspective about work out of balance.

More than our specific vocation, however, it's who we're working for that's important to God. We must understand that our work, no matter how trivial it may seem, has meaning, value, and purpose to God.

> Whatever you do, work at it with all your heart, as working for the Lord, not for men, since you know that you will receive an inheritance from the Lord as a reward. It is the Lord Christ you are serving. [1]

We don't work simply for the paycheck, or to satisfy the demands of the company—we work for God. When we approach our job from this perspective, everything changes. Our efforts begin to have meaning and we gain satisfaction from our jobs because we know the labor matters to God. In fact, our work actually becomes a means to worship

Who do you really feel like you're working for? The corporation? The boss? The family? Yourself? How would your perspective about your job change if you looked at it from God's point of view?

_____

_____

_____

_____

_____

_____

_____

_____

_____

_____

_____

_____

Do you try to see the opportunities at work to serve God? Think about your job. What is one area or one person that you, as a Christian, could have an impact on?

_____

_____

_____

_____

_____

_____

_____

_____

_____

_____

_____

_____

and glorify God. It's in the workforce that we have the opportunity to serve others in the name of Christ and to share His love with them.

We are to work with all our heart because God would expect no less. When we're on the job, our focus and attention should be one hundred percent on performing well. Even if you're stuck in a cubicle in the far corner with no one watching you, God's eyes are still there. There's nothing He does not see and He has promised that our reward is His to give out. Your paycheck, as small as it may be, is not the reward. The crowns you're laying up in heaven are.

However, as Americans, we're workaholics for the most part. Our families suffer as a result. We go about building our businesses and our practices. We build our reputations. We build our nest eggs and portfolios. But are we building in futility? Are the things we're building blessed by God?

Unless the LORD builds the house, the builders labor in vain. Unless the LORD watches over the city, the guards stand watch in vain. In vain you rise early and stay up late, toiling for food to eat—for he grants sleep to those he loves. Children are a heritage from the LORD, offspring a reward from him. Like arrows in the hands of a warrior are children born in one's youth. Blessed is the man whose quiver is full of them. They will not be put to shame when they contend with their opponents in court. [2]

What our modern culture seems to forget is that the greatest legacy we will leave behind on this planet will be our children. What is the use of a big inheritance if we don't labor to build the essential character needed for our children to handle it wisely? In striving to provide material things for our family, we have neglected the more important things our families need from us—time and attention. Psalm 127 encourages us to "build" or invest in our families. It reminds us that our children are a blessing from God, not a burden. We must be good stewards of the children that God has so graciously given us.

We need to learn to labor under God's provision and according to His plan. We need to be dependent upon God to provide for the financial needs of our families as well as to pray for His blessing and favor upon all our labor. Work should not be given priority over our families.

If we allow God to build our house and understand that He is in control, then we can cease from *futile* labor. Understand that God instituted work; we were not made for idleness. But it's anxious labor—work done to the exclusion of all else—that is an act of disobedience and a failure to trust in God to supply our every need. As we cease striving and working in vain, God will grant us peaceful sleep.

Deceived into thinking that another accomplishment or treasure will bring self-fulfillment, we continue in our work in futility. We think, "*If only I had _____, then I*

Look at your work or activity schedule. How much time does it rob from your family? How can you prioritize your life so that your family doesn't suffer from an absent parent or spouse?

What kind of hours are you working and for what purpose? Is it a short-term burst of activity to save up for a needed item, or is it a way of life for you? How is your frenzied activity a sign that you lack of faith in God?

_____

_____

_____

_____

_____

_____

_____

_____

_____

_____

_____

would finally be satisfied." Ironically, as the life of Michael Jackson illustrates, "having it all" sometimes means losing things that are fundamentally more valuable—like the peace of mind which fosters sweet sleep.

King Solomon apparently had the same issues with insomnia as the modern "King of Pop". More than having an abundance of wealth, fame, power, and pleasure, Solomon had the wisdom and insight to make sense out of all his experiences. In Ecclesiastes 5:12, Solomon describes the effects of trusting and acknowledging God in our work and how it affects our sleep. "The sleep of a laborer is sweet, whether he eats little or much, but the abundance of a rich man permits him no sleep."

Notice the difference between the rich man and the laborer—an unburdened mind. The laborer is through with his toil at the end of the shift. His work for that day is complete. The next day, the same work will be there waiting for him. It's easier for the shift-type worker to disengage his mind regarding his job.

On the contrary, those with more mentally taxing vocations, or those who have their own businesses, constantly have deadlines and decisions to make. There are always tasks that are incomplete that can preoccupy the mind. Mentally, the ambitious "rich man" is always working. His mind is always turning, thinking of ways to make his business more profitable. In other words, more money equals more stress.

These burdens will more than likely be carried to bed with him. The rich man's abundance does not provide the one thing that he desperately needs—contentment. We have to trust God's sovereignty when our day's to-do list remains uncompleted and our day's problems remain unsolved. We must learn to echo Paul when he said: "For I have learned, in whatsoever state I am, therewith to be content." [3]

Whenever we "turn in" we must also learn to "turn off" those mental gymnastics that keep us from a good night's sleep. Trusting God in our nighttime hours is just like punching a mental time clock. We must "clock out" from our labors and give our worries and concerns over to God for the duration of the evening. By doing so we release the power of God to carry and deal with these burdens in His time table and in His wisdom and grace.

Many times we have problems with sleep because we're unwilling to give up control to God. One of our greatest challenges is to learn to trust God that He will provide for us in every way at all times. For example, mothers find it extremely difficult to turn off and slow down. Sometimes the chaos that a "quiver" of children leave behind makes them feel more like a burden than a blessing! With the endless cycle of chores, there is the temptation to work well past the time the children are asleep. This just sets the mother up for losing out on the rest she needs to face the upcoming day. At some point she must throw down the towel, turn out the lights, and declare herself finished for the day.

What burdens from work are you carrying to bed with you?

83

Does knowing that God has an endless supply and abundance available to meet your needs help you to trust Him more and rest easier? If not, what keeps you from exercising your faith?

_____

_____

_____

_____

_____

_____

_____

_____

_____

_____

_____

Jesus challenges us to give up our control to Him. A wise heart recognizes that in giving God our vocational burdens, we are placing those issues with the one who can "… supply all our needs according to his riches in glory." [4]

The word "supply" in the above Philippians 4:19 verse comes from the Greek word *pleroo*, which means to fill to the brim. It means to complete, to render full. Our God is a God of endless means, of endless supply. He owns the cattle on a thousand hills! Everything on earth is His! There is no limit to what He can give.

And it's not just tangible, material things that He gives. The above verse says He will supply **all** our needs. That word "all" means everything—individually and collectively—that we can imagine, from material to emotional to spiritual in nature. Every worry, every concern, every heartache, every decision—anything you can think of can be provided by God if you'll simply turn it over to Him.

The voice of Jesus calls out to us in our distress, in those restless nights spent tossing and turning, exhausted yet unable to close our eyes. Listen to the words. Close your eyes and imagine Him before you, quietly speaking to your heart the words it desperately longs to hear: "Come to me, all you who are weary and burdened, and I will give you rest. Take my yoke upon you and learn from me, for I am gentle and humble in heart, and you will find rest for your souls." [5]

CHAPTER 9
A WISE HEART:
FINANCIAL CHOICES

As we move from an industrial economy and into the Information Age, our underlying sense of security is being threatened. Ten years ago, a job that was considered to be in a novel "cutting edge" career is now considered obsolete. In the current economic downturn, many are tossing and turning in bed due to financial pressures.

The 2009 National Sleep Foundation's *Sleep In America*™ poll shows that over one-third of Americans are losing sleep because of the current economy and personal finances. When compared with their restfully asleep counterparts, those respondents with sleep issues had more trouble working efficiently, exercising, eating healthily, having sex, and engaging in leisure activities.

Many Christians have embraced the false assumption that more money means more security. We've been taken in by a prosperity gospel, a "name it and claim it" belief system that says if we believe hard enough and speak it aloud, God will deliver. Somewhere it seems we ought to have to click our heels together three times as well.

God isn't an algorithm where you punch in preset numbers for "A" and "B" to get result "C". He isn't a god that jumps hoops based on our orchestrations. In fact, Jesus challenges us in the Sermon on the Mount to think differently about money.

Do not store up for yourselves treasures on earth, where moth and rust destroy, and where thieves break in and steal. But store up for yourselves treasures in heaven, where moth and rust do not destroy, and where thieves do not break in and steal. For where your treasure is, there you heart will be also.

The eye is the lamp of the body. If your eyes are good, your whole body will be full of light. But if your eyes are bad, your whole body will be full of darkness. If then the light within you is darkness, how great is that darkness! No one can serve two masters. Either he will hate the one and love the other, or he will be devoted to the one and despise the other. You cannot serve both God and Money.

Therefore I tell you, do not worry about your life, what you will eat or drink; or about your body, what you will wear. Is not life more important than food, and the body more important than clothes? Look at the birds of the air; they do not sow or reap or store away in barns, and yet your heavenly Father feeds them. Are you not much more valuable than they? Who of you by worrying can add a single hour to his life?

What financial areas cause you concern? What are the things that you worry about?

_____
_____
_____
_____
_____
_____
_____
_____
_____
_____

Look around you. What kind of house do you have? Do you have comfortable furniture? Do you have a dependable car that gets you where you need to go? Are you dressed in more than rags? Most Americans can answer these questions positively. If you can, what do you think contributes to your desire and want for more?

_____
_____
_____
_____
_____
_____
_____
_____
_____
_____
_____
_____
_____

And why do you worry about clothes? See how the lilies of the field grow. They do not labor or spin. Yet I tell you that not even Solomon in all his splendor was dressed like one of these. If that is how God clothes the grass of the field, which is here today and tomorrow is thrown into the fire, will he not much more clothe you, O you of little faith? So do not worry, saying "What shall we eat?" or "What shall we drink?" or "What shall we wear?" For the pagans run after all these things, and your heavenly Father knows that you need them. But seek first his kingdom and his righteousness, and all these things will be given to you as well. Therefore do not worry about tomorrow, for tomorrow will worry about itself. Each day has enough trouble of its own. [1]

We have bought into the materialist mindset that all of life revolves around money and the things that money can buy. The basic needs we have such as food, shelter, and clothing are no longer enough. We have chosen the lifestyle characterized by "more is better" and "the one that dies with the most toys wins." As was mentioned at the beginning of the chapter, we've even built a theological cocoon around ourselves, a prosperity gospel that reinforces this idolatry that suggests that God is a god of our health and wealth.

We have lived beyond our means, we have spent money we don't have, and now the roof is beginning to cave in. We've built our house on sand and now we wonder why we have difficulty sleeping! Jesus warned us about investing our attention and affections in material possessions that would not stand the test of time or eternity. As hard as it is, it's better for us to learn this lesson now, on this side of eternity, than to stand on the other side, before Almighty God, and have to give an answer for our financial actions that did nothing to please Him, help the poor, or spread the Gospel.

In the Sermon on the Mount, Jesus reminds us to set our affection and attention on things of eternal value, to seek first His Kingdom and His righteousness. Subsequently, Jesus promises to add all these things to us. We have to move our focus away from money and material possessions in order to reap the blessings that God has in store for us.

Does this mean God is going to give us that two-story mansion and a Porsche in the garage? Not hardly. We must learn that everything—*EVERYTHING*—is on loan to us from God. God says in His Word: "For the world is mine, and all that is in it." [2] We don't own these possessions; we are stewards of them. Our response to God's gifts and blessings is to return to Him what is already His for the purpose of making His name great in this world. In responding obediently to God in faith, we free God up to supply our needs, *whatever He deems those needs to be.*

In Proverbs 3:9-10, God promises to abundantly provide for those who give their best or firstfruits to God. He promises our barns filled to overflowing and our wine vats brimming over with new wine. "Honor the Lord with your wealth,

Look around you. What "toys" does your family have—adults and children alike—that are glaring examples of extravagance that is indicative of materialistic idolatry? What possessions do you have that are above the basic necessities of life? How could getting rid of some of them simplify your lifestyle and contribute to more peaceful sleep?

Think about the things you worry about and what you feel your needs are. Looking at them from God's perspective, are they truly legitimate needs or simply desires and wants? Have you replaced your desire for God and his Kingdom with material possessions?

————————
————————
————————
————————
————————
————————
————————
————————
————————
————————
————————
————————
————————

with the firstfruits of all your crops; then your barns will be filled to overflowing and your vats will brim over with new wine."

In the Old Testament, people would bring the first and best crops as an offering to God. These were not the leftovers or the wormy disease-infested crops; these crops were the finest the Israelites had to offer. In return, God would provide in miraculous ways for His people. If we could likewise learn to give God the firstfruits of our lives and labors, He would provide miraculously for us as well.

Understand this—God is not a vending machine. We can't toss in a few tokens, punch a series of buttons, and out pops a financial blessing. There are no pat formulas to be had in the Christian life. The way we feel about money and things however, relate directly to how we feel about God and His role in our lives. If we could learn to have faith in God and His ability to provide, we could have peace to sleep at night.

The one aspect about finances in today's world however, is learning to live within our means. One of the most well-known Christian financial counselors, Dave Ramsey, helps thousands of people daily to prioritize their finances more in line with prudent biblical principles. His Financial Peace University is helping thousands shed the accumulated debt in their lives and teaching them to live within their budgets. His business is booming because we have forgotten the advice of Proverbs 22:7: "The borrower is servant to the lender."

90

78 percent of American households own a credit card, about 91.1 million overall. As of 2008, the average household debt on credits cards was $10,679. According to a Nellie Mae 2004 analysis, 76 percent of undergraduate college students own credit cards. These students carry an average balance of $2,200 on these cards.

Americans today have borrowed their futures away, individually and nationally. Individually, foreclosures on homes have jumped over 30 percent from 2008. Our national unemployment rate is technically over 10 percent at this date, but realistically closer to 16 percent. Bankruptcy filings have jumped 25 percent since 2008 and are the highest since the bankruptcy law changes that took place in 2005.

We live in a cycle of perpetual debt. We have allowed ourselves to be buried under a mountain of obligations that is threatening to bankrupt us individually and nationally. The only way out of this mess is to realign ourselves with the teachings of scripture. Only by appropriating God's financial principles into our lives will we ever become free from financial bondage. This enslavement to debt helps to create perpetual tension and fear that keeps us from sleeping soundly at night.

If you recall, in the last chapter we learned of God's promise to supply all our needs. Philippians 4:19 states: "And my God shall supply all your needs according to His riches

How faithful are you in the area of tithes and offerings? Have you ever tested God to prove His faithfulness in the arena of giving?

91

How many credit cards do you carry? How many of them have balances carried over from month to month? How do you think this affects your ability to sleep peacefully at night?

_____

_____

_____

_____

_____

_____

_____

_____

_____

_____

_____

in glory by Christ Jesus." God promises to supply all our needs—not wants! Our culture has conditioned us to think that many of our "wants" are necessities.

In futility we wear ourselves out on the financial treadmill for all the things that the world tells us that we cannot survive without. Drowning in a sea of financial debt, we then we wonder why we have problems sleeping at night. A wise heart learns to distinguish between the "wants" our culture allures us with and the "needs" that God promises to provide. We must learn to echo Paul's words earlier in his final admonitions to the Philippians: "Not that I speak in regard to need, for I have learned in whatever state I am, to be content: I know how to be abased, and I know how to abound. Everywhere and in all things I have learned to be full and to be hungry, both to abound and to suffer need." [3]

I would challenge you to revisit the fourth chapter of Philippians once again. The contentment that God provides (4:11-12) and the needs that God miraculously supplies (4:19) are all set in the context of supporting the ministry of the Apostle Paul. No doubt about it, Paul is encouraging the believers in Philippi to support the ministry of the gospel.

Our wise financial choices enables us not only to sleep better at night and to support the spreading of the gospel message, but it also enables us to support those less fortunate than us with our gifts of charity. Nowhere is the wise use of our finances more exemplified than in the life of John D. Rockefeller.

John D. Rockefeller was an individual that knew how to set and accomplish financial goals. At the age of twenty-three, he became a millionaire. Becoming a billionaire by the turn of the twentieth century, he monopolized the United State's oil industry. But by the age of fifty-three, he became progressively ill with insomnia, loss of hair, and digestive problems.

An associate noted that Rockefeller could not sleep, would not smile, and nothing meant anything at all to him. He personified Solomon's description of how the rich man's abundance hinders his ability to sleep. Rockefeller's insomnia was so severe that he lost sleep over the most trivial of things—like losing $150 on an insurance deal. Preparing for death, Rockefeller changed gears and began channeling his assets towards philanthropic endeavors. To the surprise of his doctors, Rockefeller miraculously began to improve shortly after adopting a lifestyle of generosity.

Ironically, Rockefeller lived to the ripe old age of ninety-eight. He continued to give a portion of his earnings throughout the rest of his lifetime. Today, his legacy of the Rockefeller Foundation continues to contribute to missions and various charities all over the world. Rockefeller learned a hard lesson: the finances that God allows to flow into our lives must not be hoarded, but channeled back into God's work and invested in the lives of others.

In modern Israel, the Sea of Galilee flourishes with life. The water which flows into the Sea of Galilee eventually flows

What debt obligations keep you up at night? Do you even make enough to pay your obligations from month to month? What can you do to take control of your financial future?

out into the Jordan River. Further south, the Dead Sea (being below sea level) takes in the run-off of the Jordan, but has no outflow. As a result, its high salt content from years of evaporation makes it stagnant and incompatible with maintaining life.

In stark contrast to the Sea of Galilee, the Dead Sea is useless and has no evidence of life. We must learn, in the area of finances, to become a channel where a significant portion of our income flows out of our lives and into God's work. Otherwise, our lives become like the Dead Sea—lifeless and useless. God's plan for our finances always involves generosity.

From before the time that Abraham stepped out in faith, leaving his homeland and journeying to a country he knew nothing about except in promise, God has been providing for His people. He has talked to us from burning bushes, from pillars of fire, through His prophets and priests, through His son, Jesus, and finally through His Word, exhorting us to live frugally and by faith. We have not heeded that call. We're reaping the results of that disobedience, but we're not forsaken. In our darkest moments and our deepest needs, God will provide a way. If we can wrap our hearts and our faith around that one truth, sleep will not be so very far away from us.

CHAPTER 10
A WISE HEART:
PHYSICAL ACTIVITY AND DIET

Do you have a physically taxing job or do you sit at a desk all day? How much exercise do you get in an average week?

I t has long been known that physical activity contributes to restful sleep. The result of hard physical labor is that we get tired. When we tire physically, we sleep—especially if that work is for the Lord. However, in our modern age, most of us don't have physically demanding jobs. Our lifestyles don't require physical labor and thus, we must replace that with exercise. Let's re-examine Ecclesiastes: "The sleep of a laborer is sweet, whether he eats little or much, but the abundance of a rich man permits him no sleep." [1]

Medical literature is beginning to align with what the Bible has been suggesting for years. A 2003 study at the Fred Hutchinson Research Center showed that postmenopausal women who exercised every morning for one-half hour had significantly less problems going to sleep. A National Sleep Foundation study also suggests that daily early-afternoon exercise increases the ability to fall asleep as well.

The Bible suggests that there is a link between our physical activity and the ability to sleep well. A wise heart will incorporate a lifestyle of exercise into his daily routine.

While the Bible doesn't have specific mandates about physical exercise, we are told that the body is the temple of the Holy Spirit (1 Corinthians 6:19-20) and that we are no longer our own since we have been bought at great price by God. We are told to honor Him with our bodies, and physical exercise would certainly fit into this category. The only thing we should guard against is the extreme and being caught up in vanity—allowing exercise and our bodies to become idols that replace our worship of God.

The Greek word that "honor" comes from in the passage from 1 Corinthians is *doxazo*. It means to celebrate, to adorn, to make the knowledge of something or someone manifest and acknowledged. Through the practiced care we give our bodies, we celebrate the life that God has bestowed upon us. It becomes an act of worship. Remember, the goal of exercising should be to improve our physical health, to gain more energy so that we may devote more of ourselves to spiritual goals.

Another thing self-help sleep books discuss, in addition to exercise, is diet and the need to adjust or change your diet to maximize sleep potential. One thing that's suggested is making the evening meal the smallest one of the day. We should abstain from eating right before bedtime as well, to optimize sleep. Someone said we should eat breakfast like a king, lunch like a prince, and the evening meal like a pauper. Although there are multiple dietary habits which contribute to a good night's sleep, the weightier issue is the quality and amount of food we consume on a daily basis. Instead of treating the body like God's temple, the tendency is to treat

Do you not know that your body is a temple of the Holy Spirit, who is in you, whom you have received from God? You are not your own; you were bought at a price. Therefore honor God with your body.
1 Corinthians 6:19-20 NIV

Are you neglectful of your body? What habits do you have that misuse or abuse your body? What can you do to reach a higher level of physical activity?

Think about the food you have consumed just today. Was it healthy and nutritious? Or was it loaded with sugars and had little nutritional value at all? Is this normally how you eat? What steps can you take to begin eating more healthfully?

it more like a garage—a place to stuff all kinds of things that we really don't need.

There are many sleep disorders in the United States that are linked to obesity. For example, obesity is the underlying cause of most cases of obstructive sleep apnea and gastroesophageal reflux disease. These problems don't begin overnight, but rather insidiously, through the course of several years, as we indulge in more food than we need. We live in a culture that has an abundance of food, and it's always a temptation to eat more food than our body requires.

There are new scientific findings linking obesity and poor sleep. In 1999, scientists discovered a hunger hormone called *ghrelin* which is made in the stomach and pancreas. Ghrelin affects the hunger centers in the brain by increasing your hunger and slowing down your metabolism. Studies have shown that people who do not sleep properly make more ghrelin and thus are prone to weight gain—producing a self-perpetuating vicious cycle. Scientists are now working on antibodies that block the effects of ghrelin on the brain. While we are learning about the genetic predispositions toward obesity, we still must discipline ourselves to resist gluttony. Nothing can replace the discipline of self control.

Many of the foods we eat that are rich in refined sugar predispose us to insulin resistance, or possibly diabetes. Fad diets only feed the cycle of weight loss and weight gain to the point that we become either obsessed with our weight or we stop caring altogether. Our diets should be something we do; they should not be how we define ourselves. More than anything else, a wise heart must understand that there is no substitute for the discipline of self-control in the area of our appetites. Eating itself is not the sin; it's gluttony to the point of disobedience of biblical principles that reflects the loss of self-control. "Do not join with those who drink too much wine or gorge themselves on meat, for drunkards and gluttons become poor, and drowsiness clothes them in rags." [2]

Do you find yourself in stressful situations where you just cannot get enough food to satisfy you? Do you find yourself craving the carbohydrate-rich donuts and sugary foods without end? God tells us to call on Him for our needs. Pray now that God will give you the strength to start treating your body with the respect it deserves.

Our culture of abundance encourages us to "live to eat." In contrast, a biblical perspective encourages us to learn to "eat to live." Our health, our physical longevity, and our sleep are all affected by our weight. Conquering our self-indulgence in the area of eating requires discipline, common sense, and dependence on the Holy Spirit to develop self-control. Self-control is a manifestation of the filling of the Holy Spirit in our lives, according to Galatians 5:22-25: "But the fruit of the Spirit is love, joy, peace, patience, kindness, goodness, faithfulness, gentleness and *self-control*. Against such things there is no law. Those who belong to Christ Jesus have

What steps can you take to honor God with the care you give yourself?

crucified the sinful nature with its passions and desires. Since we live by the Spirit, let us keep in step with the Spirit."

Do you realize that you can ask God to provide you with self control? Self-control isn't something that you can attempt under your own weak willpower. Ask God now for the strength to resist temptation and the ability to flee from it.

As we learn the internal discipline of self-control, we can begin the arduous process of controlling our appetites and overindulgence of food. When we do so, we can prevent many of the disorders that can potentially rob us of needed sleep.

CHAPTER 11
A WISE HEART:
A PROACTIVE APPROACH TO HEALTH

What physical issues are you, or someone close to you, suffering with right now? Do you or they feel, subconsciously, that somehow a lack of faith is contributing to the continuation of the illness or condition?

I n reading this book so far, one could falsely jump to the conclusion that all sleep issues come from spiritual origins. A wise heart understands the interrelatedness of the spiritual, physical, and emotional aspects of sleep and proactively pursues health in all these areas of life. This is one aspect of loving the Lord with all our heart, soul, mind, and strength. [1] A comprehensive approach to health and sleep helps us to obey Jesus' great commandment. Wisdom also will help us learn to discern between a spiritual, a physical, or a psychological cause of our insomnia. As we learn about sleep medicine, we will learn to discern between conditions that require the expertise of a doctor and those that can only be cured by the Great Physician.

Many Christians believe that it is unspiritual to seek medical attention for sleep issues, that using modern medicine is an indication of a lack of faith. In fact, a Barna 2006 telephone survey reveals that evangelical Christians are less likely to enjoy seeing their doctor than other faith-based groups. We sometimes think that if we will just believe enough, all our physical problems will go away.

The Bible in no way discourages us from visiting a doctor. In the ninth chapter of John, Jesus heals a man that was blind from birth. Jesus takes saliva, mixes it with dirt, and puts it on the blind man's eyes. Jesus then tells the man to go wash his eyes in the pool of Siloam. "So the man went and washed, and came home seeing." [2] In this passage we see the complementary relationship of medicine, faith, and miracles in the blind man's healing. "What medicine?" you might ask.

In ancient times saliva was considered to be a medicine. Saliva was used for all kinds of maladies. But Jesus doesn't just use saliva—he mixes it with dirt. Remember, in creation, God performed another miracle with dirt: "The Lord God formed the man from the dust of the ground and breathed into his nostrils the breath of life, and the man became a living being." [3]

In this interaction with the blind man, we see both medicine and the miraculous. But interwoven in the narrative there's another important ingredient—the obedience and faith of this man as well. Jesus gave the blind man some very specific directions. Apparently the pool of Siloam was a good distance to walk—especially for someone who couldn't see! But in faith he obeyed Jesus completely. In this particular instance, Jesus used the medicine, the person's faith, and a dose of the miraculous in restoring the blind man's vision.

Many times when I'm counseling patients about surgery, I remind them of this threefold process of healing. There's my part (the medical); their part (faith/trust/compliance); and God's part (the miraculous). All three are just as important in the equation of healing.

The National Sleep Foundation's *Sleep in America Poll*™ found that 64 percent of those questioned noted they had

Can you think of a time when you or a loved one was very ill and it took a combination of medicine, prayer, and faith to assist in healing? When was that?

problems sleeping several nights per month. However, only half of that group (32 percent) ever discussed their sleep issues with a physician. Interestingly, of the group that had discussed their insomnia issues with their health care provider, nearly half (42 percent) were diagnosed with a sleep disorder. [4] It seems that people are not discussing their sleep issues with their doctors, and a majority are needlessly suffering from treatable sleep disorders.

Almost everyone would call their doctor if they thought they needed emergency surgery, but people seem to be more reluctant to address chronic sleep issues with their physician. Many times people assume there is a stigma associated with seeing their doctor about poor sleep. They think that it shows they have an emotional or psychological issue and that their insomnia is a sign of weakness.

Another misconception people have is that all the doctor has to offer is sleeping pills that will lead down a road of addiction. This is not true. If persistent insomnia is plaguing you, your doctor may recommend a sleep clinic to evaluate your condition. This usually requires an overnight sleep study to determine the cause of your sleeplessness. Many times diet and lifestyle changes, along with behavior modifications, may be the initial focus of the treatment plan.

When sleep problems begin to affect your quality of life, consult your doctor. Studies have shown that it typically takes about twelve years for a person with insomnia to see a doctor. More than half of the patients with insomnia never, ever visit a physician for this problem. The longer a sleep problem continues, the more conditioned people seem to become to having more sleep issues. Consequently, a cycle develops which is sometimes much harder to break the longer it continues.

Having all the appropriate information ready for your doctor when you go for your visit may help him to make a diagnosis and discuss treatment options with you. One way to provide relevant information to your doctor is by keeping a sleep diary. A sleep diary should consist of what time you go to bed, the amount time it takes you to go to sleep, the number of awakenings per night, the time you get up in the morning, and noting how long it takes you to go to sleep after you awake at night. Keeping this for a week or so before your doctor's visit will help your doctor understand your sleep issues. A sleep diary is provided in the back of this book.

Remember, the Bible does not disapprove of using modern medicine to get a good night's sleep—but it does seem to disapprove of putting our trust entirely in modern medicine rather than in God. King Asa displeased the Lord because he excluded God while suffering from disease: "… yet in his disease he did not seek the Lord, but the physicians." [5] We must understand that medicine is one means which God can use to heal the body. Athough doctors can administer treatments, only God can do the healing.

Have you approached your family care doctor or another health care provider for help with your sleep issues? If not, what are your reasons?

_____

_____

_____

_____

_____

_____

_____

_____

_____

_____

In his book *Prayer: Asking and Receiving*, author John R. Rice notes: "There are a number of scriptures which show it is no sin to consult a physician, if it be done in faith, depending on God to use the doctor, and no sin to take medicine if it be in faith, depending on God to bless and use the medicine which He Himself has supplied in nature for mankind .... In any case, whether with medicine or without, it is God who does the healing. He should have the glory; our trust should be in Him, not in men." [6]

We do not assemble a health care team because all our faith and confidence is in them. We use our health care team as one of the components in our overall approach to health. When we do our part, we can rest easy knowing the end result is in God's very capable hands. We must always remember that it is God that directs the outcome.

Understanding of sleep disorders has truly advanced over the last twenty years, and treatments are improving. More importantly, so is our awareness and ability to treat those disorders. There is a wealth of information available about our health, fitness, and good sleep. At the end of this chapter, you will find some sleep websites that may be useful to you as you learn about sleep medicine.

Understanding basic patterns of sleep

Sleep helps restore proper functioning of our body, helps us to consolidate memory (much like defragging a hard drive), and helps preserve our psychological and emotional well-being. A basic knowledge of sleep can empower us just as a better understanding of nutrition can improve our health.

As we sleep we progressively cycle through five stages. We slip into deeper stages of sleep through the first four phases known as the non-rapid eye movement levels. The last stage, or rapid eye movement stage (REM sleep) is the most important phase. After we finish REM sleep, we resurface into the lighter stages of sleep, restored physically and emotionally. Any interruption in this sequence of sleep, especially missing the REM phase, will hinder the restorative role of sleep that we need to function.

Sleep patterns change as one's physiology changes throughout life. Ask any mother of a newborn, and she will agree that babies initially have very erratic sleep patterns. Toddlers and young children tend to have the most psychological resistance in going to bed (thus stressing the importance of bedtime routines). This is the age however, when humans experience the most profound sleep/wake patterns.

Those with children have all seen how quickly sleep can overwhelm children when they tire. Kids can instantaneously fall to sleep on a rock. And when they awake, they are fully alert and full of energy. As we move into the teen years, the biological clock seems to shift so that many teens become "night owls," sleeping late most mornings. In the teenage years, more than ten hours of sleep per day can be associated with rapid growth spurts.

As we move into adulthood, we tend to have more erratic sleep habits, going to bed earlier and having more awakenings at night. Our ability to sleep changes as we age. When we get into our senior years, we find that we sleep far fewer hours in one setting, but generally nap more often.

Be informed about sleep disorders

There are over one hundred known sleep disorders which affect us in all ages of life. Each inhibits various stages of the sleep cycle, causing insufficient sleep. The most common sleep disorders are:

Insomnia

A conservative estimate says that over 60 million Americans suffer from insomnia. Insomnia is defined as difficulty falling or staying asleep which consequently has a negative impact on one's daytime function. The typical features of insomnia include:

- Difficulty falling asleep
- Frequent awakenings during the night
- Difficulty returning to sleep
- Waking up too early in the morning
- Unrefreshing sleep
- Daytime sleepiness
- Difficulties concentrating
- Daytime Irritability

Primary insomnia is an internal abnormality in the timing of the sleep-wake mechanism. Secondary insomnias are more from external sources such as chronic pain from arthritis, cancer, or peripheral vascular disease. Insomnias can be short-term from life stressors or long-term from chronic health conditions.

Insomnia can be broken down into several different patterns. The first includes problems falling asleep from what are, many times, emotional issues and sleep-habit issues. The next category includes the inability to stay asleep at those times when, despite us not having any problems going to sleep, something wakes us up.

Obstructive Sleep Apnea

Obstructive sleep apnea is found in over 2.5 million Americans. People who suffer from this condition literally choke or stop breathing as the muscles relax during sleep. Over 90 percent of cases of sleep apnea are linked to obesity caused by excess fat closing down the airway. This type of sleep apnea is known as Pickwickian Syndrome. Other causes of sleep apnea may include enlarged tonsils, nasal polyps, or a deviated nasal septum that hinder the inflow of air while breathing.

If left untreated, sleep apnea can lead to serious health issues. Hypertension, heart disease and various psychiatric disturbances can arise as the syndrome persists. The primary treatment for most cases of obstructive sleep apnea is weight

If you are suffering from insomnia or sleep deprivation, what symptoms are you manifesting? What are those tell-tale signs that let you know you need rest?

_____

_____

_____

_____

_____

_____

_____

_____

_____

_____

_____

109

loss and/or continuous positive airway pressure, or CPAP. CPAP provides pressure to keep the upper airway muscles from closing off as the muscles relax during sleep.

Restless Legs Syndrome

Restless Legs Syndrome is a phenomenon where one experiences leg discomfort during sleep that is only relieved by frequent movement of the legs. It is sometimes described as a creepy-crawling or a painful, numbing-type sensation over the legs. People with this syndrome feel the urge to move their legs to relieve the sensations. Typically, the feelings are more noticeable at night when one is still or resting. In contrast to other diseases that worsen with motion (such as peripheral vascular disease and neuropathies), the symptoms of Restless Leg Syndrome improve upon leg motion.

I've seen patients who can't rest because of gastroesophageal reflux disease that wakes them up with severe chest pain and heartburn as acid irritates the lining of their esophagus. Many older people cannot sleep because of urinary retention caused by benign prostatic hypertrophy and frequent urination. Frequently, many suffer insomnia because of chronic pain issues that hinder the ability to comfortably wind down and enter the deep stages of sleep. There are hundreds of conditions that can hinder effective sleep. Most people live unaware that their sleep issues may be influenced by an underlying medical problem.

Poor sleep is associated with, and can lead to, ailments such as:

- Depression
- Heart disease
- High blood pressure
- Irritability
- Obesity
- Delayed psychomotor responses
- Slurred speech
- Nausea
- Tremors
- Fibromyalgia
- Immune system impairment

Your brain's decision-making ability is greatly hindered when you are sleepy. Problem-solving skills are non-existent when your brain is muddled. Long-term sleep deprivation can lead to hallucinations or death. Lab rats denied sleep died within three weeks. Sleep is not a choice. It's a necessity.

Develop Good Sleep Hygiene

The majority of people suffering from insomnia are suffering from problems with poor sleep habits. Sleep hygiene, including simple behavioral changes that can be made, often makes a dramatic difference. Most of the following suggestions require using a little common sense at bedtime.

1. Establish a rhythm of going to bed and waking up at the same time.

2. Never use your bed for anything other than sleep or sex with your spouse. In other words, do not pay your bills, watch TV, or read the newspaper in bed prior to going to sleep.

3. Avoid drinking a lot of fluids before going to bed to prevent unnecessary wake-ups for the bathroom.

4. Minimize caffeine and alcohol consumption prior to going to bed.

5. Exercise routinely, but do not do so within three to four hours before going to sleep. Exercise gets your adrenaline pumping and will make sleep impossible.

6. Minimize light and sound in your bedroom.

7. Don't eat too much, too late in the evening.

8. If you cannot go to sleep initially, get up and do something for a little while and then try again.

I would encourage you to search these websites for further information about sleep. These sites will get you started on educating yourself about sleep medicine in general.

1. SleepNet: www.sleepnet.com

2. National Sleep Foundation: www.sleepfoundation.org

3. American Sleep Disorders Foundation: www.asda.org

CHAPTER 12
A RESPONSIVE HEART

Every happening, great and small, is a parable whereby God speaks to us,
and the art of life is to get the message.
~Malcolm Muggeridge ~

I will bless the Lord who has given me counsel;
my heart also instructs me in the night seasons.
~Psalm 16:7 NKJV~

Everyone knows the importance of a wake-up call. We set our alarm clock to go off at a certain time in the morning so that we're not late for an event. It may be something as straightforward as going to work every day, or getting up early to go duck hunting. We may be leaving early so we can catch a flight for our vacation. Usually, when we are sleeping in a hotel, we call the concierge and they will give us a wake-up call at the indicated time. We have these calls for the simple reason that we do not want to miss whatever engagement that we have scheduled.

In a similar fashion God, unbeknownst to us, sometimes schedules a wake-up call for us—a moment or a message that He does not want us to miss. Although these wake-up calls can occur at any hour, many times they happen during the night.

Remember the Lord never slumbers or sleeps. He is just as active in our lives during our sleeping hours as during our wakefulness. We naturally assume that God chooses to direct, lead, and speak to us during our wakefulness, but we forget that God is there twenty-four hours a day, seven days a week. God, at His convenience, may chose to speak to us and draw us to Himself through insomnia or problems with sleep. Although this may make us uncomfortable, from God's prospective this is a small price to pay to position our hearts so that we can be attentive to what He has to say.

Has it ever crossed your mind that in those instances where you can't fall off to sleep or when you wake up in the middle of the night, that the Lord of the universe may have something personal to say to you?

Why would God chose this method? My wife understands this better than anyone. She has developed this long arduous routine of talking with our children and saying their prayers right before bedtime. In contrast, when I put the children to bed it is more of a "go-to-sleep and shut-up" type approach. My wife, in her wisdom, has learned that by spending time with our children in the transition between wakefulness and sleep, she is able to seize on those teachable moments when our children have no other distractions.

It is a simple fact that the crammed schedules, daily activities, and unlimited distractions of our modern, fast-paced society can drown out God's voice in the daytime hours. God is a gentleman; He will not force Himself into our lives. Therefore at night, as we transition into sleep, our minds and emotions begin to slow down and we begin to

Have you ever had a moment so enveloped in silence that you could almost hear the audible voice of God? Instead of fighting for sleep, have you ever considered using that time to seek God?

115

reflect on the day. God sees the opportunity to have our undivided attention and sometimes uses the stillness and solitude of the night to speak with us.

We know that God works this way because there are stories in the Bible that show it. One of the best biblical illustrations of a "wake-up call" is found in the life of a young boy named Samuel. God revealed Himself to the boy at night during his sleep. As Eli and Samuel were winding down for the night, God showed up.

> The boy Samuel ministered before the Lord under Eli. In those days the word of the Lord was rare; there were not many visions. One night Eli, whose eyes were becoming so weak that he could barely see, was lying down in his usual place. The lamp of God had not yet gone out, and Samuel was lying down in the temple of the Lord, where the ark of God was. Then the Lord called Samuel. Samuel answered, "Here I am." And he ran to Eli and said, "Here I am; you called me." But Eli said, "I did not call; go back and lie down." Now Samuel did not yet know the Lord; the word of the Lord had not yet been revealed to him. The Lord called Samuel a third time, and Samuel got up and went to Eli and said, "Here I am; you called me." Then Eli realized that the Lord was calling the boy. So Eli told Samuel, "Go and lie down, and if he calls you, say, 'Speak, Lord, for your servant is listening.'" So Samuel went and lay down in his place.

The Lord came and stood there, calling as at the other times, "Samuel! Samuel!" The Samuel said, "Speak, for your servant is listening." [1]

In this passage we learn a heart-breaking thing—the Word of the Lord was rare. What a sad testimony for a people that had God speaking to them from burning bushes and out of pillars of fire! We are just as bad today, drowning out the voice of God with our endless pursuits during the day. God has no other choice but to speak to us at night because we're not around to listen at any other time! There are several things that we need to understand and observe about our God.

A Wake-up Call From a PERSONAL God:

God repeatedly called the young boy by his name—Samuel. Samuel's name can be translated as "the God who hears". God had heard the prayers of his mother for a child and responded with the birth of their boy Samuel. God was intimately acquainted with every aspect of the young boy.

The Lord saw how Samuel ministered under Eli's authority. God saw tremendous potential in this young boy. Instead of sending an angel, God showed up in person to speak to Samuel in an intimate, personal way. God's approach and call to us is still a one on one, personal encounter.

God knows our circumstances, our fears, our joys. He is intimately acquainted with every minutia of our lives—past,

Are the thoughts and questions that come to your mind at night indicative of God's voice speaking to your spirit? Can you look at your nighttime restlessness and see the hand of God?

_____

_____

_____

_____

_____

_____

_____

_____

_____

_____

_____

_____

_____

_____

Psalm 139:13 says: "For you created my inmost being; you knit me together in my mother's womb." This passage is telling you that God created not just your body, but your intellect, your heart, your soul, and your spirit… everything about you! Have you ever tried to determine what God's plan is for your life? If not, why? If you have, are you living it out?

_____

_____

_____

_____

_____

_____

_____

_____

_____

_____

present and future. He knows everything about us, from the number of hairs on our heads to the amount of debt hanging over our head. He created us. He fashioned us in the womb with a specific personality, interests, and abilities all because of His divine purpose. God has a specific plan for each of us individually—not just for the Billy Grahams of this world.

So many times we misunderstand how God deals with us. We see God as some distant impersonal detached entity that has more important things to do than to be concerned about our issues, challenges, and circumstances. Our understanding of who God is determines our expectations of how God will communicate with us. I am reminded of the contemporary chorus that we sometimes sing at church.

> *I have a maker*
> *He formed my heart*
> *Before even time began*
> *My life was in His Hands*
> *He knows my name*
> *He knows my every thought*
> *He sees each tear that falls*
> *And hears me when I call.*
> *("He Knows My Name" by Tommy Walker © 1996.)* [2]

A Wake-up Call From a PERSISTENT God:

Let's look at the passages of 1 Samuel 3:1-10 in the context of the events going on at that time. Eli was a priest and judge in ancient Israel, before the rule of kings. He was of the Levitical tribe, the ones dedicated to priesthood. But Eli and his sons had dishonored and disrespected God. Eli had allowed his love for his sons to overshadow his love and devotion to God. His sons, Hophni and Phinehas, had treated God, His altar, and His sacrifices with contempt. God had withdrawn His presence from Eli and Israel because of their wickedness. That's why the Bible says that God rarely spoke in those days.

However, Samuel's heart was young and still open to God. Unfortunately, he had never heard the voice of the Lord and as such, was confused. To Samuel's credit, he was persistent in wanting to respond to whoever was talking. Eli was not so far gone that he didn't know what was happening, however. He could still recognize the workings of God and he gave Samuel a great piece of advice. He encouraged him to be still and to answer: "Speak, for your servant is listening."

God is equally persistent in His communication toward us. God, in His grace, engages us again and again, trying to get our attention. We, like Samuel, fail to recognize God when He is speaking to us. In regard to insomnia, we look for every other possible answer except the fact that God may be trying to get our attention. But God persistently continues to beckon. Like Samuel, we should respond to God's voice in the darkness.

Are you responding to God's voice? Are you making yourself available to God? What steps can you take to make sure that you are responding as Samuel did, saying to God, "Speak, for your servant is listening."

2 Timothy 2:15 tells us to "Do your best to present yourself to God as one approved, a workman who does not need to be ashamed and who correctly handles the word of truth." The word "present" in this case means to come into fellowship and intimacy with. Casual Bible study and short trite prayers won't get it. What can you do to set aside time each day to be intimate with God?

Moving Closer to Hear His Call:

Also notice that this passage emphasizes where Samuel was sleeping. Samuel is sleeping next to the lamp, close to the Ark, and the holy articles of God. At the time of the Old Covenant, the Ark represented the dwelling place of God on earth. God's presence was known to be there. Samuel was sleeping in close proximity to the very Presence of God, and was positioned to be ready to hear from God.

Someone once said: "You're as close to God as you choose to be!" James 4:8 admonishes us: "Come near to God and he will come near to you." In order to hear from and be responsive to God, we must be close by. We gain proximity to God primarily through His Word and prayer. God continues to use these two means to speak to us. Unlike the days of Samuel however, the New Covenant declares that God's presence is now within each believer. The Holy Spirit indwells us and speaks to us as we come near.

Adjusting Our Priorities to Hear His Call:

Samuel had his priorities in order. He did not seem to be bothered by being disturbed from his sleep. Although his understanding was limited, he was available and willing to be obedient, first to Eli and then to the Lord. Samuel responded with "Here I am." He was ready and willing to serve, showing that his priorities were in line with God's. Obedience and desire to hear God's voice outweighed his desire to sleep.

120

We too must learn to adjust our priorities to be in tune to God's voice. Hearing God's voice when He desires to speak to us should become one of the main pursuits of our life. And if that means losing sleep to hear from God—then so be it! Hearing God's voice needs to take precedence in our lives whether in the midnight hour or during the day.

We sometimes hear what we have trained ourselves to hear. My wife and I have learned this principle through the years. Sometimes after I've had a restful night of sleep, my frustrated wife will inform me that one of the children was crying all night, and I slept right through it. In fact, our house could be burning down and my children could be screaming bloody murder, and I would probably sleep through the whole ordeal. On the contrary, when my pager or cell phone goes off with a call from the hospital, I immediately wake up and respond to the call. My ears have been conditioned to hear selectively what they want (or need) to hear.

When my wife needs my attention in the middle of the night, she will just simply page me or call me on my cell phone instead of trying to wake me from my coma. Sometimes, that is the only way to wake me up. "He calls his own sheep by name and leads them out. When he has brought out all his own, he goes on ahead of them, and his sheep follow him because they know his voice." 3

How would you describe your ability to decipher God's voice? What steps are you taking to train yourself to hear God when He speaks?

_____
_____
_____
_____
_____
_____
_____
_____
_____
_____
_____

121

NOTE: Learning to hear God's voice can be like walking in unchartered territory. Sometimes we need help to do so. Recommended reading, besides God's Word, includes A. W. Tozer's *The Pursuit of God*, Dallas Willard's *Hearing God: Developing a Conversational Relationship with God*, and *How to Listen to God* by Charles Stanley.

Responding to God's Call:

Samuel was willing for God to interfere with his life. While Eli the priest ultimately recognized that the Lord was calling Samuel, Samuel wisely followed his elder's advice and responded accordingly.

"Speak, Lord, for your servant is listening," is a statement giving God permission to interfere in our lives. When we ask God to "speak" we are giving Him permission to say whatever is on His mind. We are giving God complete "freedom of speech" in regard to our lives. We may not want to hear what God has to say … but it's what God needs to tell. In fact, the message Samuel received that night was a difficult one.

When we respond to God with this statement, "Speak, Lord, for your servant is listening," we're telling God that He has our undivided attention; we are ready to hear exactly what He has to say to us. It does God no good to speak until we are ready to listen, and we must let God know that we are listening. Beth Moore, in her Bible study *Believing God,* states succinctly that God does not speak just to hear the sound of His own voice or to be heard by others. She cites Isaiah 55:10-11 to show that the intent of God speaking is to accomplish something.

In addition, this statement acknowledges that we are ready to respond and act upon the message that God delivers. When we acknowledge Him as Lord and that we are His servants, we imply that we are ready to be obedient to the message that He has prepared for us.

Read the scripture passage again. Samuel not only heard the voice of God, he responded. Samuel *got up* out of his bed. He didn't understand everything that was going on at the time, but *he was willing to get up out of his bed and be obedient.*

You may not understand everything in regard to your sleep issues. When you awaken in the middle of the night, instead of tossing and turning or rolling over in your bed—get up! Instead of counting sheep, we must learn to talk to the Shepherd! Kneeling at your bedside and giving God permission to speak may be the most productive thing that you could do in this situation. The One who knows your name, who knows your every thought, who sees each tear that falls, may be trying to *get your attention.*

This event marked a change in the course of Samuel's life. After learning to hear from God, Samuel continued to hear

"As the rain and the snow come down from heaven, and do not return to it without watering the earth and making it bud and flourish, so that it yields seed for the sower and bread for the eater, so is my word that goes out from my mouth: it will not return to me empty, but will accomplish what I desire and achieve the purpose for which I sent it." (Isaiah 55:10-11) What do you feel God is trying to accomplish in your life?

_____
_____
_____
_____
_____
_____
_____

from God throughout his life. Just think of what Samuel would have missed out on had he failed to recognize God's voice—being used for God's purposes for *the whole nation of Israel*. We don't know what God's leading will mean for our lives. We don't know if His plan is within our families or encompasses a nation. He only asks that we respond, "Speak, Lord, for your servant is listening."

Think of what you could be missing out on by not hearing God's voice. Perhaps the next time you are dealing with problems with sleep, you should fall to your knee and say, "Speak, Lord, for your servant is listening". Perhaps you have failed to recognize why you're having sleep issues. Your insomnia may be a "wake-up call" from the God of the universe. He may be trying to get your attention to reveal to you the course He desires for your life.

After his first encounter with the Lord, Samuel continued forward in his relationship with God. "The Lord was with Samuel as he grew up, and he let none of his words fall to the ground. And all Israel from Dan to Beersheba recognized that Samuel was attested as prophet of the Lord. The Lord continued to appear at Shiloh, and there he revealed himself to Samuel through his word. And Samuel's word came to all Israel." [4]

While Samuel's experience with the Lord was a positive example of how to respond to God in the nighttime hours, the disciples nearly missed out on a great opportunity at the

Mount of Transfiguration.

About eight days after Jesus said this, he took Peter, John and James with him and went up onto a mountain to pray. As he was praying, the appearance of his face changed, and his clothes became bright as a flash of lightning. Two men, Moses and Elijah, appeared in glorious splendor, talking with Jesus. They spoke about his departure, which he was about to bring to fulfillment at Jerusalem. Peter and his companions were very sleepy, but when they became fully awake, they saw his glory and the two men standing with him. As the men were leaving Jesus, Peter said to him, "Master, it is good for us to be here. Let us put up three shelters—one for you, one for Moses and one for Elijah." (He did not know what he was saying) [5]

Peter, James, and John nearly let the opportunity of a lifetime get away from them because of the desire to sleep. Here the incarnate God was being transformed before them, Moses and Elijah were miraculously there with them, and they were discussing God's future plans. And the disciples were dozing! Although they got to see a glimpse of heaven, I wonder if they ever regretted missing the opportunity of seeing the full glory of the Lord Jesus Christ on this side of eternity.

Have you ever experienced a moment when you are suddenly awakened from sleep for no apparent reason? It may be the Lord's guidance—maybe a person crosses your mind or a new way of thinking about a problem you're facing. Get up and pray, or at least write it down so you can reflect and pray on it in the morning. Don't let your desire for sleep overwhelm your desire for God and His voice. You can never tell what you may be missing.

A responsive heart has learned that God schedules wake-up calls to "counsel" and "instruct us in the night seasons." Our desire should be to draw so close to God that we can hear His heartbeat.

CHAPTER 13
A DISOBEDIENT HEART

Some Christians have the impression that sleeping well always indicates a sign of a healthy relationship with God. Wrong! This conclusion does not measure up to scripture. Sometimes the exact opposite is true! In some instances, too much sleep can reflect a heart of disobedience.

Got Maggots?

Recently, I had a flashback to an experience long forgotten–and for good reason. A physician never knows what to expect as the curtain is drawn back to examine a patient in the emergency room. We hope for the best but anticipate the worst.

The bed behind the curtain I stopped at that day held a nice man who happened to be a diabetic. This very pleasant diabetic had forgotten to take his shoes off for quite some time—probably a month or so. As the socks were peeled off this man's foot, a putrid, foul odor began to fill my nostrils. The gangrene which was advancing up his leg was what we anticipated. The emergency room nurses shrieked in horror at what we didn't anticipate—*maggots*.

As these happy little maggots were devouring the remnants of this man's foot, old memories began to fill my mind. I reminisced back to my first semester as a medical student in Houston, Texas. Eager for action, my roommate and I signed up to observe in the emergency room at Ben Taub General Hospital during our first year of basic science. There I was first introduced to the characteristic smell of wet gangrene. Lo and behold, there they were—maggots climbing their way up this homeless man's eroding leg. As a young impressionable student, this picture was imprinted deep in the recesses of my memory. Now, as a more mature and crusty surgeon, it's old hat. You know, "been there done that, just chop it off and move along."

The first thought that entered my mind those many years ago was: how could a person live in such a state of denial and neglect that they were unaware of squiggly little worms consuming a portion of their dying flesh? Medically, we understand that diabetics are prone to develop a peripheral neuropathy of the feet, a condition where the nerves slowly deteriorate until they lose all sensation in the feet and lower legs. A person with peripheral neuropathy can burn the bottom of their feet or step on a nail and not even be aware of it.

As believers, we can develop a spiritual neuropathy where our hearts become calloused and ultimately disobedient. In this condition our ability to identify things that could potentially be harmful to us is altered. Our flawed spiritual nervous system becomes unable to identify and transmit potential dangers that could impair our spiritual health. Sin, like a maggot, begins to feast on us, taking advantage of our weakened defense system.

Have you ever used sleep as a means to escape the reality of life around you? Did you find it just easier to close your eyes and sleep, ignoring problems rather than to face them?

129

Scripture presents several examples of this condition in a disobedient heart and how it can manifest itself in our sleep patterns. With Jonah, sleep is portrayed as a delusional escape from reality. In the life of Sampson, we see sleep as a sin of overconfident presumption. The book of Proverbs describes the sleep of laziness or idleness. And finally, with the disciples, we see careless or complacent sleep in the Garden of Gethsemane.

Sleep as an Escape

As we review the life of Jonah, we see that Jonah had a disobedient heart. One of the manifestations of this disobedience was a sound sleep. For those of you that went to Sunday school, you may remember this story with the little flannel board figures of the prophet Jonah. Sleep for Jonah in this instance was an escape from the realities facing his life.

> The word of the Lord came to Jonah son of Amittai; "Go to the great city of Ninevah and preach against it, because its wickedness has come up before me." But Jonah ran away from the Lord and headed for Tarshish. He went down to Joppa, where he found a ship bound for that port. After paying the fare, he went aboard and sailed for Tarshish to flee from the Lord. Then the Lord sent a great wind on the sea, and such a violent storm arose that the ship threatened to break up. All the sailors were afraid and each cried out

to his own god. And they threw the cargo into the sea to lighten the ship. But Jonah had gone below deck, where he lay down and fell into a deep sleep. The captain went to him and said, "How can you sleep? Get up and call on your god! Maybe he will take notice of us, and we will not perish." [1]

We know the rest of the story. Jonah's disobedience was discovered, and he was thrown overboard and swallowed by a great fish. We get a glimpse of Jonah's heart at this point. His heart had become so calloused and insensitive to God's voice that he was oblivious to the circumstances threatening his life. Jonah was using sleep to escape reality. In so doing, he put himself, the sailors, and even an entire nation in jeopardy.

Here we see that under the right circumstances, sleep can be a manifestation of a heart hardened to the voice of God. Jonah receives the ultimate wake-up call. The captain rebukes him, asking him to call on his god, oblivious to the fact that Jonah is both the cause and the cure to their dilemma. He asks Jonah a very penetrating question: "How can you sleep?"

Jonah's ability to sleep in the bottom of the ship while the fearful storm was raging on at sea reflects a complacent, apathetic, insensitive, and self-absorbed attitude. Instead of repenting of his disobedience or praying for God's

Are there situations in your life, your community, or the world at large that you should really be concerned about, but are not? Has apathy set in, numbing you to the truth of the situation? Do you feel it's useless to be so overly worried about the problem?

_____
_____
_____
_____
_____
_____
_____
_____
_____
_____
_____
_____

131

intervention (or even helping the sailors save the ship!), Jonah displays features of this spiritual neuropathy.

In case you haven't noticed, our present world is in a mess. We now live in the daily threat of terror from radical Islamic groups. North Korea and Iran continue to develop nuclear arms in defiance of sanctions from other world countries. At home, many have lost their jobs with little hope of employment. More Americans are now unable to retire due to the loss of their savings in the economic collapse. America is now strapped in generational debt. Our national values are changing as most Americans adopt postmodern attitudes and reject Christian beliefs and values.

However, like the sailors crying to their gods for deliverance and trying everything to keep the ship afloat, people in our society are struggling for answers and hope. We, like Jonah in the boat, are the ones able to provide the answer. The words of the captain are still relevant for us today: "Why are you sleeping?"

We could discuss how we believers are all figuratively "asleep" spiritually, and how we need to wake up to the realities of our day. But in a literal sense what we need to do is put the amount of hours we sleep under the lordship of Christ. The Bible never tells us that we need eight hours of sleep every night. On the contrary, the Bible warns against tendencies to oversleep.

Presumptive Sleep

The second way our sleep can reflect disobedience is seen in the life of Samson. This is the sin of presumptive sleep.

Then she said to him, "How can you say, 'I love you,' when you won't confide in me? This is the third time you have made a fool of me and haven't told me the secret of your great strength." With such nagging she prodded him day after day until he was tired to death. So he told her everything. "No razor has ever been used on my head," he said, "because I have been a Nazirite set apart to God since birth. If my head were shaved, my strength would leave me, and I would become as weak as any other man." When Delilah saw that he had told her everything, she sent word to the rulers of the Philistines, "Come back once more; he has told me everything." So the rulers of the Philistines returned with the silver in their hands. Having put him to sleep on her lap, she called a man to shave off the seven braids of his hair, and so began to subdue him. And his strength left him. Then she called, "Samson, the Philistines are upon you!" He awoke from his sleep and thought, "I'll go out as before and shake myself free." But he did not know that the Lord had left him. Then the Philistines seized him, gouged out his eyes and took him down to Gaza. Binding him with bronze shackles, they set him to grinding in the prison. [2]

Satan ruins men by rocking them asleep, flattering them into a good opinion of their own safety, and so bringing them to mind nothing and fear nothing, and then he robs them of their strength and honour and leads them captive at his will .... If we sleep in the lap of our lusts then we shall certainly wake in the hands of the Philistines.

Matthew Henry Commentary on the Whole Bible

Are there areas of sin in your life that you have simply ignored or deliberately overlooked? Have you avoided bringing them to the altar of God and confessing because you really don't want to give up the behavior?

Samson was aware that Delilah was after the source of his strength and power, and was attempting to subdue him for the Philistines. Yet he still slept in confidence that everything would be the same as before. Sampson presumed that he could follow sensuality and promiscuity and still have the favor or blessing of God in his life. Sampson went to sleep that evening in Delilah's lap, overconfident that he could handle things on his own. But God allowed his sin to catch up with him. Samson awoke, impotent and pitiful. Samson reflects the negative side of not allowing the Lord to be our protection and relying instead on our own resourcefulness.

Idle Sleep

The book of Proverbs notes that disobedience can manifest itself as idle sleep. Proverbs warns us that a lack of disciplined sleep habits can lead to our financial and spiritual demise.

> Do not love sleep or you will grow poor; stay awake and you will have food to spare. [3]

> Go to the ant, you sluggard; consider its ways and be wise! It has no commander, no overseer or ruler, yet it stores it provisions in summer and gathers its food at harvest. How long will you lie there, you sluggard? When will you get up from your sleep? A little sleep, a little slumber, a little folding of the hands to rest and a poverty will come on you like a bandit and scarcity like an armed man." [4]

134

Yes, there are times to sleep. But there are also times to get up, work, and fulfill the plans and purposes that God has prepared for us. We must learn to make wise decisions about when and how much sleep we require, and then discipline our lives accordingly.

God has uniquely created in each of us a specific amount of sleep required per day. Dr. Micheal E. Debakey routinely functioned on four hours of sleep per day and lived to be 100 years of age. Similarly, Thomas Edison thrived on four to five hours of sleep. We may need to experiment in determining our physiologic sleep requirements. We can determine our sleep needs by setting our alarm clock back fifteen minutes earlier every week. As we begin to notice fatigue and decreased mental sharpness, we will learn our personal sleep requirements.

I suggest you use this extra time to develop the practical discipline of a daily devotion. In developing this discipline of prayerfully hearing God's instructions and aligning our agenda with God's, we can be more effective and efficient in carrying out our mission for the day. We will be able to focus on God's agenda for our day instead of cramming in unnecessary activities into our schedule.

Jesus demonstrated this during His life. He would get away at times and have fellowship and prayer with the Lord. In Mark 1:35 we see this clearly: "Very early in the morning, while it was still dark, Jesus got up, left the house and went

Is your day filled with idle pursuits? Are there activities that you need to give up in order to fulfill the role in life that God has planned for you?

The Bible tells us to be diligent, that our adversary is a roaring lion seeking to devour us. "Be self-controlled and alert. Your enemy the devil prowls around like a roaring lion looking for someone to devour." ⁵ Have you recognized Satan as an adversary worthy of attention and avoidance, or do you consider him a myth or of no importance?

off to a solitary place, where he prayed." This passage records that the previous night, Jesus was busy healing the sick and teaching. Most of us after a long day and night of ministry would have the temptation to sleep in and catch up on some rest. But Jesus models for us the power of the "mind over the mattress."

Careless or Complacent Sleep

One of the big headlines in New York recently read: "Texting teen falls into manhole." On Staten Island, fifteen-year-old Alexa Longueira fell five feet into raw sewage, suffering cuts and bruises and even losing her shoes. Why didn't she see it? She was distracted by her cell phone, texting her friend.

God desires to steer us clear of those "manholes" in life. One way God does this is by encouraging us to get up or stay up, and praying for awareness of the dangers in our path. In addition to grieving the work of the Holy Spirit in our lives, disobedience to God's prompting in the still of the night may lead to some major spiritual failures.

In the garden of Gethsemane, Jesus forewarns the disciples of the potential manholes that they were unaware of. Filled with good intentions, the disciples tried to stay up with Jesus in the garden the evening prior to the crucifixion. But weary from the day, they slept a careless, disobedient sleep.

Then Jesus went with his disciples to a place called

Gethsemane, and he said to them, "Sit here while I go over there and pray." He took Peter and the two sons of Zebedee along with him, and he began to be sorrowful and troubled. Then he said to them, "My soul is overwhelmed with sorrow to the point of death. Stay here and keep watch with me." Going a little farther, he fell with his face to the ground and prayed, "My Father, if it is possible, may this cup be taken from me. Yet not as I will, but as you will." Then he returned to his disciples and found them sleeping. "Could you men not keep watch with me for one hour?" he asked Peter. "Watch and pray so that you will not fall into temptation. The spirit is willing, but the body is weak." He went away a second time and prayed, "My Father, if it is not possible for this cup to be taken away unless I drink it, may your will be done." When he came back, he again found them sleeping, because their eyes were heavy. So he left them and went away once more and prayed the third time, saying the same thing. Then he returned to the disciples and said to them, "Are you still sleeping and resting? Look, the hour is near, and the Son of Man is betrayed into the hands of sinners. Rise, let us go! Here comes my betrayer!" [6]

The indifferent sleep of the disciples wasn't because they didn't love the Lord. They loved Jesus fervently. They just didn't see the necessity of staying up and preparing for an unseen battle over the horizon. Sleeping was the most expedient thing that they could do. Their "spirit was willing, but their flesh was weak."

Many of you who experienced college remember those all-nighters. These were the nights during final exams when you would stay awake, cramming information that you had studied (or maybe not) for the final comprehensive exam. You did everything in your power (whatever it took) to prepare for the exam that would determine your final grade for the semester.

Similarly, there are times when we need to prepare spiritually for the tests that we know we will encounter. Three times in the garden Jesus encouraged the dozing disciples to stay awake, to "watch and pray" in preparation for the upcoming trials that the disciples would face. Unbeknownst to them, they would all fall away because of their lack of preparedness. Fatigued by the day, they chose to sleep rather than be vigilant in prayer with the Lord. The disciples had no idea the degree of testing and challenge that lay on their horizon.

But Jesus knew. Jesus knew that the time for His arrest, trial and crucifixion had arrived. Jesus knew that the faith of the disciples would be tested and found lacking. Therefore, Jesus forewarned them of the imminent spiritual battle and encouraged them to prepare.

Jesus also knew that while the disciples were sleeping, Satan was awake, working through Judas, preparing to destroy the faith of His followers.

Leaning back against Jesus, he asked, "Lord, who is it?" Jesus answered, "It is the one to whom I will give this piece of bread when I have dipped it in the dish." Then dipping the piece of bread, he gave it to Judas Iscariot, son of Simon. As soon as Judas took the bread, Satan entered into him. "What you are about to do, do quickly." Jesus told him, but no one at the meal understood why Jesus said this to him. Since Judas had charge of the money, some thought Jesus was telling him to buy what was needed for the Feast, or to give something to the poor. As soon as Judas had taken the bread, he went out. And it was night. [7]

Satan, lurking in the shadows of the night, has manholes prepared for us. Satan's plan is simple—he desires for us to fall into the sewage and filth of sin, ruining our faith in God and our credibility with others. He wants to soil our influence with others and trap us into bondage. Like the evening of the Lord's Supper, our enemy seems to be peculiarly active in the nighttime hours.

Statistics have shown that the night watch is always busier for the police. Assault and robbery are twice as prevalent in the nighttime hours. Moreover, a recent Internet study has revealed that we are becoming a nation of night surfers. The increase in the use of the Internet is primarily due to increased traffic on pornography sites, Internet games, and YouTube.

The Bible says Satan is real. He is a real enemy seeking to destroy the elect of God. How can knowledge of this enemy help you avoid the traps set for you in the future? What steps should you take to protect yourself from this enemy?

139

The Internet can be a great tool used for many good purposes, but it also gives us instantaneous access to sites that can trap us into pits of bondage. With the Internet, sin and its consequences are just a click away. Perhaps the roaring lion knows that we are more susceptible at the edge of night when we are tired physically and emotionally, with few people around to hold us accountable. Satan lulls us into believing that he also is retiring for an evening of rest, but just as God is active in the twilight hours, our crafty adversary is operating in the darkness.

God sees the manholes before us and knows where and how we can fall. He desires for us to live victoriously, weathering the storms that He knows we will face. This is why Jesus encouraged the disciples to watch and pray because temptation was knocking at the door. We need to learn to be sensitive and obedient to the Spirit's tug on our hearts, to the inner prodding to get up and pray. We know that this may be God encouraging us to prepare our lives for the upcoming storm.

There will be times when we will be facing a trial or temptation, and losing sleep is a small price to pay in order to be prepared for the upcoming tests on our horizon. It is important as believers that we learn to avoid careless sleep and be on our guard through the night when the time is appropriate.

The disciples, unfortunately, failed the test and fled the scene after Jesus gave Himself over to the angry mob. In the next chapter we'll see the contrast of how the Lord prepared Himself for the upcoming spiritual storm.

CHAPTER 14
A SERVANT'S HEART

Has there ever been an experience in your life where you prayed with all your heart and soul for God to allow the cup of suffering to pass by you?

_____

_____

_____

_____

_____

_____

_____

_____

_____

_____

_____

_____

We may need to voluntarily deprive ourselves of rest in order to fulfill God's immediate purpose for our lives. The Holy Spirit may be prompting us to pray, or leading us into some kind of work during the time we would usually sleep. We see no greater example of this than the Lord Jesus Himself in the Garden of Gethsemane. Knowing that His time had come, Jesus spent sleepless hours praying to God, preparing Himself for the coming trial and crucifixion. In Luke 22:39-46 we see how Jesus struggled in prayer. This was a time of preparation, asking His Father for the strength to endure the accusations, beatings, and physical and emotional torture that he would encounter within the next twenty-four hours. He was asking God for the strength to endure what He knew was imminent.

Jim Cymbala, pastor of the Brooklyn Tabernacle in New York and author of *When God's People Pray*, recalls the night he could not sleep and was lead to pray. He ended up praying all night. He kept asking God why he wanted him to pray, but no answer was given. The next day, September 11, 2001, the World Trade Center collapsed when the United States was attacked by terrorists. That night, God had prepared him to minister to many of the families that suffered in the 9-11 tragedy.

In the gospels, we see that Jesus was struggling with God's

will. Jesus was asking if this cup could be taken from Him. In other words, He wanted to see if there was any way He could avoid the next hours. From a human standpoint, He was dreading the torture that He would endure. His praying was so intense that He sweated drops of blood. The part of our humanness that Jesus was experiencing was the facet of our makeup that shrinks from any kind of suffering, especially death.

However, as He prayed and sought God's will, He understood that there was no other way for mankind to be redeemed except by the cross. He submitted to God's will, as Luke 22:42 records: "'Father if thou willing, remove this cup from me; yet not my will but thine be done.'"

At the same time Jesus was struggling with the anticipated horrors of the cross, He was also praying for the disciples and for us. [1] He was praying that His disciples and future followers would have victory over the evil one, be sanctified in truth, that they would have fullness of joy, that they would be kept in the Father's hand, and that they would be sent into the world to proclaim the good news of Jesus.

Think of the selflessness that Jesus demonstrated. In our minds, we would think that Jesus would need a good night's sleep to be fresh and prepared for the challenges that He would meet with the Sanhedrin the following day. Instead, Jesus selflessly struggled in prayer. With self-control and composure, He carried out the plan of salvation amidst the hatred of His accusers and the pain of the cross.

How does praying for others, even while we're in the midst of our own struggles, help us to grow spiritually? What do we learn when we take our eyes off our own trials and join in prayer and compassion for others?

143

Christ is the ultimate example of a servant. We see in Philippians 2:3-7: "Do nothing from selfishness or empty conceit, but with humility of mind regard one another as more important than yourselves; do not merely look out for your own personal interests, but also for the interests of others. Have this attitude in yourselves which was also in Christ Jesus, who, although He existed in the form of God, did not regard equality with God a thing to be grasped, but emptied Himself, taking the form of a bond-servant, and being made in the likeness of men." (ASV)

This willingness to deprive Himself of rest and pray for God's higher purposes appeared to be an ordinary occurrence in Jesus's earthly ministry. Jesus surrendered sleep prior to choosing the disciples and preaching the Sermon on the Mount [2]; prior to the miracle of walking on the water [3]; during the Transfiguration [4]; and during the miracles of His ministry in Galilee. [5] Jesus stayed awake and prayed: we are encouraged in these passages to follow His example. Thus the question "Why are you sleeping?" is still as valid and poignant today as it was when Jesus was with His disciples in the garden, There are times when we need to be sensitive to God's prompting, get up from our bed, and pray.

Remember the story about Peter's calm sleep in prison? The church in Jerusalem was "earnestly praying to God for him" during the night, setting a hedge of peace and protection around him with their prayers. Our prayers are the avenues that God uses to work in our lives and the lives of others.

Peter, James, and John displayed their complacency for the Lord when they slept in the garden. They should have been ministering to Jesus, encouraging Him with their prayers, asking for strength for themselves during this upcoming time. Instead, they chose the path of careless indifferent sleep.

Some people take the stand that it's God's will for you to sleep soundly. Although this may be true, it is only partly true. Sometimes, it is God's will for us to get up. Sometimes taking up our cross and following Jesus means denying ourselves sleep whenever we are called. Have you ever been burdened at night to pray for another person or to go and help someone else? We often miss opportunities for the Lord to use us in His kingdom because of our laziness or unwillingness to get up out of our beds. The challenge for most of us is winning the battle of the mind over the mattress. Our spirit is willing but our flesh is weak.

> Yet there is considerable truth in the idea that revivals are born after midnight, for revivals come only to those who want them bad enough. [6]

> No, there is no merit in late hour prayer, but it requires a serious mind and a determined heart to pray past the ordinary into the unusual. Most Christians never do. And it is more than possible that the rare soul who presses on into the unusual experience reaches there after midnight. [7]

Some of the most significant events in Jesus's earthly ministry grew out of occasions of surrendered sleep. How do you think this principle should be practiced in your life? What do you think God could do in your life as a result of this kind of surrender?

145

Can you look at circumstances or relationships in your life and see a need for fervent prayer or attention? Are you willing to make the necessary sleep sacrifices to be the hands and feet of God to those in need?

_____

_____

_____

_____

_____

_____

_____

_____

_____

_____

_____

_____

Praying is not the only activity that we may need to lose sleep over. The apostle Paul, in describing the burdens of his ministry in Corinth, showed there were many nights in which he deprived himself of sleep in order to carry out his calling in the ministry. II Corinthians 11:27 states: "I have been in labor and hardship, through many sleepless nights, in hunger and thirst, often without food, in cold and exposure." (ASV) II Corinthians 6:4-5 says: "But in everything commending ourselves as servants of God, in much endurance, in afflictions, in hardships, in distresses, in beatings, in imprisonments, in tumults, in labors, in sleeplessness, in hunger..." (ASV)

Earlier we learned about how God moved in power in the midnight hour while Paul and Silas worshiped in the jail in Philippi. But there's more to the story. Once delivered, Paul and Silas didn't fall to sleep oblivious to the needs of the others around them. Paul shared the story of the gospel to the jailer and his family. After meeting his spiritual needs, Paul baptized the whole family and fellowshipped with them till the wee hours of the morning. Paul and Silas didn't punch the time clock and say to the Philippian jailer: "Thanks for your help; we'll baptize you in the morning." The missionaries selflessly sacrificed their sleep to serve the spiritual needs that were presented to them. [8]

On another occasion, Paul preached all night to the church in Ephesus. A young boy named Eutychus fell into a deep sleep and fell three stories down to his death. Paul miraculously healed the young man and then apparently went on preaching until morning. After being up all night, Paul then departed on his way, continuing on in his missionary journeys. [9]

In the book of Joshua, we see numerous occasions where the armies of Israel willingly deprived themselves of sleep to conquer the Promised Land. In Joshua 10:1-14, the Israelite army marched uphill during the night, eighteen miles from their camp at Gilgal, for a surprise attack on the armies of the South camped at Gibeon. The battle continued all day with a miraculous victory under Joshua's leadership.

With more enemies to conquer, Joshua prayed to God to allow the sun to stand still. God answered his audacious prayer and suspended the laws of nature, allowing God's armies to utterly defeat their enemies. After they finished the battle, they marched back down to their camp at Gilgal. Can you imagine the fatigue of two or more days of wakefulness and physical exertion? However, there's no evidence that anyone complained. Joshua and the armies of Israel probably did not want to miss a thing. Seeing God working in miraculous ways, defeating their enemies and fulfilling His promises for their lives was enough to motivate their hearts toward their goal, negating any concerns over the loss of sleep.

There are many other ways that we can demonstrate a servant's heart by surrendering sleep to fulfill God's purposes in our lives. It may mean a mother getting up out of bed

Do you have a willing heart, the kind that is prepared to sacrifice its own comfort and needs for the sake of someone else? Are you people-focused or me-focused?

to care for her sick toddler, or going to the hospital and encouraging and being with a friend who is suffering. It may mean sitting with an elderly parent or being available in the wee hours to a friend in need. Physicians, nurses, firefighters, pastors, and many others are oftentimes called to sacrifice sleep to serve others with specific needs that require their expertise.

Are you willing to be the eyes, ears, hands, and feet of our Lord? If you truly want to develop a servant's heart, then offering a sacrifice of sleep may be what the Lord is calling you to do.

CHAPTER 15
A SEPARATED HEART

The Old Testament presents several episodes of God distressing the sleep of several kings to establish His purposes. Shakespeare's diagnosis was correct: "Uneasy lies the head that wears a crown." [1]

In the book of Esther, God disturbs the sleep of King Xerxes and protects the nation of Israel from Haman's anti-Semitic plot to annihilate the Jewish nation. Similarly, in Genesis, the dreams and insomnia of the pharaoh are the tools used to ultimately elevate Joseph to prominence, and to bless Jacob and his family. Darius, king of Persia, could not sleep because of his concern over Daniel, who was in the lion's den. The most interesting of these accounts is where God communicates truth to Nebuchadnezzar. In the second chapter of Daniel, we see how the living God orchestrates this encounter with the Babylonian king through an episode of insomnia. God, in His grace, relentlessly pursues this pagan king to reveal His character and sovereignty.

> During the second year that Nebuchadnezzar was king, he had such horrible nightmares that he could not sleep. So he called in his counselors, advisors, magicians, and wise men, and said, "I am disturbed by a dream that I don't understand, and I want you to explain it."

They answered in Aramaic, "Your Majesty, we hope you live forever! We are your servants. Please tell us your dream, and we will explain what it means." But the king replied, "No! I have made up my mind. If you don't tell me both the dream and its meaning, you will be chopped to pieces and your houses will be torn down. However, if you do tell me both the dream and its meaning, you will be greatly rewarded and highly honored. Now tell me the dream and explain what it means."

"Your Majesty," they said, "if you will only tell us your dream, we will interpret it for you." The king replied, "You're just stalling for time, because you know what's going to happen if you don't come up with the answer. You've decided to make up a bunch of lies, hoping I might change my mind. Now tell me the dream, and that will prove that you can interpret it."

His advisors explained, "Your Majesty, you are demanding the impossible! No king, not even the most famous and powerful, has ever ordered his advisors, magicians, or wise men to do such a thing. It can't be done, except by the gods, and they don't live here on earth." This made the king so angry that he gave orders for every wise man in Babylonia to be put to death, including Daniel and his three friends. [2]

Nebuchadnezzar, king of Babylon, was the most powerful monarch of the ancient civilized world. This proud,

You may be in a position similar to these ancient kings. You may have the perfect job, enough money, a nice house, and the average American family with a spouse and 2.1 children. (I've never figured out how to have .1 children, but that's the statistics!) Even if you go to church and consider yourself religious, you may have demonstrated through your actions that you really feel no need for God, that you're doing fine all on your own. Is this your attitude? Could God be trying to show you, through your restless sleep, that you have a need for Him that nothing else can satisfy?

Do you find yourself picking out the parts of the Bible that conflict with your lifestyle, desires and wants, tossing them aside? Have you decided to fashion a god after your own image? Do you think the almighty God of the universe is willing to be contained in such a manner?

temperamental king ruled a vast empire from Egypt to Greece. He had anything he could desire and everything at his disposal. As a young sovereign king, he had limitless time, options, money, and resources. There is no indication prior to this episode that he had any concern about where he would spend eternity. He had no perceived emptiness or absence of meaning in his life. He displayed no felt needs or awareness of sin and separation from God. He had no desire or need to know the God of Israel. In fact, upon conquering Jerusalem, he ransacked the Temple and took all the gold and temple artifacts to Babylon. Nebuchadnezzar, king of Babylon, appeared to be the sovereign ruler of his life.

He was, however, religious. He worshipped a multitude of powerless pagan gods, but they were subservient to his agendas and desires. Then, apparently unannounced and uninvited, God abruptly interrupts his life through a brief time of insomnia and dreams.

Why? Why would God even try to communicate with this king? The king appeared to be a hopeless case. But God, in His grace, chose to intervene in the life of Nebuchadnezzar. There is no case too hard for God. There is no heart too hard that He cannot penetrate. The Bible says: "The Lord is not slow in keeping his promise, as some understand slowness. He is patient with you, not wanting anyone to perish, but everyone to come to repentance." [3]

Our spiritual situation hasn't changed that much since ancient times. Like Nebuchadnezzar, our society has embraced a pluralistic, post-modern concept of God that conveniently has no real power. We desire to be sovereign over our lives. Like going to Luby's or another all-you-can-eat buffet, we like to pick and choose the parts of various religions that are suitable for our particular lifestyle.

Some would argue that it really doesn't matter what you believe, as long as you are sincere. They say if your religious beliefs are true for you, then they are a valid choice. They like to say there are many ways to reach God or heaven, but this would be in direct contradiction to what the Bible says.

Like King Nebuchadnezzar, you may have been looking for your answers in all the wrong places. Nebuchadnezzar found that the magicians, astrologers, and wise men were impotent in helping him to answer his problems. Similarly, we tend to look for answers in the all the wrong places. Ultimately, Nebuchadnezzar encountered God through the help of the prophet Daniel.

God desires to intervene in your life. Your sleep issues may not be as dramatic as Nebuchadnezzar's, but it may be God's vehicle to reveal Himself and communicate truth to you. Our God is an engaging God. He loves us and desires to enter into a relationship with us. Even if you have no apparent need for God in your life, He calls to you. He will be relentless in His pursuit of you. God will use whatever He so desires to accomplish this goal. From God's prospective, a little loss of sleep is a small price to pay for the opportunity to have a relationship with you for eternity.

What is the only way to heaven and a relationship with God? Find a Bible verse to support your position.

_____

_____

_____

_____

_____

_____

_____

_____

_____

_____

_____

_____

153

Do you feel that your relationship with God is superficial and without much substance? Could your sleep issues be the Holy Spirit calling you to a deeper relationship with your Creator?

_____

_____

_____

_____

_____

_____

_____

_____

_____

_____

_____

In his quest to disprove the validity of Christianity, Josh McDowell shares how God pursued him as he laid down to sleep.

> I returned to the United States and to the university, but I couldn't sleep at night. I would go to bed at ten o'clock and lie awake until four in the morning, trying to refute the overwhelming evidence I was accumulating that Jesus Christ was God's Son. [4]

Does this describe your struggle with the Lord of Sleep? God may be allowing a little sleep debt in your life to make you aware of His plans to cover your sin debt. If this is the case, the next few paragraphs of this book should be life changing.

First we must understand that we are separated from God because of our sin. Romans 3:23 tells us: "For all have sinned and fall short of the glory of God." Isaiah 59:2 states: "But your iniquities have separated between you and your God, and your sins have hid his face from you, that he will not hear." (KJV)

So here is the dilemma—God loves us and desires a relationship with us, but He is also a holy God that cannot tolerate any sin. It is impossible for us to have the relationship that God desires unless our sin is dealt with. Furthermore, the Bible says the wages of sin is death.

If the whole Bible could be distilled into one verse, it would be Romans 6:23: "For the wages of sin is death, but the

gift of God is eternal life through Jesus Christ our Lord."
If you think about it, the Bible records the history of man's
separation from God due to his sin, and God's plan of
reconciliation. Death means not only the eventual physical
one, but more importantly, a spiritual death—a separation
from God.

We do not have the ability or desire to meet God's moral
standard. The payment or wages of our sin—death—is what
we've earned and deserve. Fortunately, God gives us His gift,
the gift of His son Jesus Christ. Through Jesus, God was able
to deal with our sin problem and bridge the gap between
our sinfulness and His holiness. Romans 5:8 says: "But God
commendeth his love toward us, in that, while we were yet
sinners, Christ died for us." (KJV) And while the gift is free
for mankind, it was very costly to God.

Jesus Christ was fully God and fully man. He never sinned,
living a perfect life. However, when they crucified Him on
the cross, an amazing thing happened. He absorbed our sin
and took the punishment that we deserved so that we might
have the opportunity to be reconciled to God.

Notice that God's part is a gift. It's free. Nowadays, we seem
to be skeptical about free gifts, like those free offers on the
Internet that always ends with your name on some list where
they badger you on the phone or with emails. But God's gift
for you is totally free—you can't earn it or jump through
some religious hoop to get it.

Have you ever really made that commitment to Jesus, inviting him to be the Savior of your soul? Do you understand that nothing you do—no amount of church attendance, good works, or moral actions—can make you acceptable before a holy and just God? There is only one way back into a right relationship with God—through Jesus Christ.

155

Remember that we mentioned earlier that sleep is a gift from God. It must be received. God may be withholding the gift of sleep to allow you to stumble onto His greatest gift— eternal life. Going to bed knowing that everything is right between you and God is one of the best ways you can get a good night's sleep. Knowing that the sins of your past are forgiven, and that you now can experience the abundant life Christ promised, is the most comfortable pillow that you can have. To have a vibrant relationship with God is the greatest asset a person can ever possess.

By the way—what are you waiting for? Are you waiting for lightning to strike before making your decision? If you study the life of Nebuchadnezzar, you will learn that that's exactly what he did. He made a superficial decision to allow God in his life. Eventually, God had to humble him completely by taking everything away from him just to show Nebuchadnezzar who was the boss. Why wait? Don't follow in the footsteps of this ancient king. A better example to follow is found in the life of the Phillipian jailer. Awakened by God through an earthquake, the desperate jailer asks Paul: "Sirs, what must I do to be saved?" [5] Decide to make Jesus the ruler of your life. If you have never experienced a personal relationship with Jesus Christ, I would encourage you to do so. Here's how:

Repent of your sins

First, this involves taking ownership of the wrongs that you have done, in thought, word or action, and telling

God something along these lines: "God I know that I have wronged both You and others, and I alone am responsible for what I have done in Your sight." This is what people mean when they talk about "confessing" their sin.

Second, repentance means that you change your mind about sin. You begin to take on the same attitude that God has about the things that you have done wrong. You've heard folks talk about the term "turn or burn"? Well, what it means is that we change the direction of our lives, especially how we look at sin. Repentance is different than remorse, or feeling sorry for your sin. Repentance involves an attitude or willingness to change.

Believe in the Lord Jesus Christ

As the apostle Paul proclaimed to the Philippian jailer: "Believe on the Lord Jesus Christ, and you will be saved." [6] This is where faith comes in. Part of this involves an understanding that there is nothing that you can really do to obtain salvation on your own. Through Jesus, however, it's already been done for you. Believe that Jesus took the punishment for your sin, the punishment that you deserved, and dealt with it on the cross. Then you must receive this free gift by faith.

That's about as simple as I can make it. I would suggest you talk to God about your decision. It's more than saying a prayer that saves you; it's believing that God has heard your prayer and accepted you through Jesus Christ.

157

Please talk to someone you trust—maybe a friend or pastor or somebody in your family. Please let us know about your decision at www.SurrenderedSleep.com.

CHAPTER 16
AN ENDURING HEART

We will never fully understand the meaning of suffering on this side of eternity. Do we suffer primarily due to the influence of sin in our lives, or is it simply more a part of the human experience? Can we learn anything from our trials, or is simply enduring enough?

How do we cope when there seems to be no end in sight to the sleepless nights? We pray in faith for deliverance, for better sleep, and yet heaven remains silent. We suffer from chronic sleep disorders like obstructive sleep apnea, Restless Leg Syndrome or chronic pain, and sleep continues to elude us. We've seen the best doctors, used all the sleep hygiene formulas and even said all the right prayers, and still insomnia and sleep deprivation plagues us. Like Asaph, we cry out to God, declaring: "You hold my eyelids open; I am so troubled that I cannot speak." [1]

And even though the Lord of sleep does not owe us an explanation, He assures us that we can have a strengthened heart that helps us to endure our struggle with those sleepless nights.

Consider the suffering of Job. Listen to the intensity of Job's struggles with sleep:

> So I have been allotted months of futility, and nights of misery have been assigned to me. When I lie down

I think, "How long before I get up?" The night drags on, and I toss till dawn. My body is clothed with worms and scabs, my skin is festering....when I think my bed will comfort me and my couch will ease my complaint, even then you frighten me with dreams and terrify me with visions, so that I prefer strangling and death, rather than this body of mine. I despise my life; I would not live forever. Let me alone; my days have no meaning. [2]

Job had endured almost every kind of imaginable calamity. He lost his family, his health, his prosperity and even the respect of his wife and friends. Job was experiencing the pain of skin sores and abscesses as he tried to sleep every night. He had been "clothed" with scabs and worms and pus. Job's infection was all over his body, and unlike today, there were no antibiotics or home health nurses available. His physical pain was multiplied by the emotional turmoil of the loss of all his children, the frayed relationships with his wife and friends, and the constant reminder by these so-called friends that his problems were his entire fault! (Is this beginning to sound familiar?)

He describes "nights of misery" that have been allotted him, the dreams and fearful visions that plague and frighten him. He yearns for the morning, because at least the daytime offers some distractions from his suffering. But the worst dimension of his suffering seems to be the spiritual dimension, the unanswered question of "Why?" that is directed at God. The breadth and depth of Job's sleep issues are overwhelming.

When we look at Job's situation, we can see that on some level our sleep problems will fit into one (or maybe several) of the categories that Job encountered. We may have a physical problem such as sleep apnea or Restless Leg Syndrome that we must chronically endure, or maybe the pain of poor leg circulation, chronic back pain, or incurable cancer that makes it impossible to get comfortable at bedtime. We could be struggling with the emotional loss of a loved one, such as Job experienced in the untimely loss of his children. We may be enduring the pain of broken relationships such as wayward children or alienated family that makes us toss and turn at night. Maybe the worst category we're faced with is the spiritual—the "God-why-are-you-doing-this-to-me—don't-you- care?" question that we ask about God's love and sovereignty.

Whatever the source of the issues that we deal with in the nighttime hours, whether they be physical, emotional, relational, or spiritual, we can learn from Job's demeanor through his sufferings. There are several things we can glean from Job's example that will help us to nurture an enduring heart.

Not always explanations or deliverance—only a deepened understanding and experience of God.

God is not obligated to explain the reasons behind our

insomnia. Job questioned God as to why he was going through all of his suffering, but God's only answer to Job was: "Where were you when I laid the foundations of the earth? Tell Me, if you have understanding." [3] In like vein, God continued asking the questions that clearly put Job in his place as the created, not the Creator. As God revealed His greatness, majesty, wisdom, and power to Job through a battery of penetrating questions, Job was humbled into silence and submission.

That is potentially the greatest thing we need to know through any trial, not just our sleep issues. We may never have an explanation on this side of heaven for the suffering we endure. That suffering, however, should drive us to understand the unchanging character of God. The assurance that God is faithful, good, and working out His will and character in our lives will help us to persevere despite our sleep issues.

God did eventually deliver Job, but the greatest blessing for Job was coming to understand and know God in a deeper, more personal way. In the same way, we must also accept that God is the potter and we are the clay. If He chooses to use sleep issues to mold us into His image, then we must learn to submit to His will.

Our hearts can also be strengthened by the example of Paul's thorn in the flesh. As with Job, God allowed Satan to discourage and torment Paul.

We can also experience "thorns" that hinder our sleep. What's the thorn that's hindering your sleep?

———————————

———————————

———————————

———————————

———————————

———————————

———————————

———————————

———————————

———————————

———————————

———————————

To keep me from becoming conceited because of these surpassingly great revelations, there was given me a thorn in my flesh, a messenger of Satan, to torment me. Three times I pleaded with the Lord to take it away from me. But he said to me, "My grace is sufficient for you, for my power is made perfect in weakness." Therefore I will boast all the more gladly about my weaknesses, so that Christ's power may rest on me. That is why, for Christ's sake, I delight in weaknesses, in insults, in hardships, in persecutions, in difficulties. For when I am weak, then I am strong.[4]

What specifically was Paul's thorn? Was it a physical deformity such as poor eyesight? We may never know, and it's probably better that way. What's remarkable about the apostle is not the thorn, but his mature response to this irritation.

A thorn is another word for splinter. All of us have experienced an irritating splinter in our foot or hand that we couldn't get out. Every time we rubbed or touched that area, the pain reminded us that it was there; it was a constant irritation. Also, the longer the thorn is present, the worse the swelling and inflammation can become.

A Peculiar Gift and Change of Focus

One Christmas I decided to put my wife to the test. I gave her multiple gifts (jewelry, perfume, and such) but placed them all in boxes and packages of common kitchen utensils like pots, pans, and blenders. My wife soon understood the peculiar twist to my gift wrapping and let me back in the house. She had realized that appearances could be deceiving. As she began to dig deeper into her "gifts," she noticed that it was only a disguise for a gift more precious and costly.

Likewise, God has a way of sending His gifts in peculiar wrappings or packages. Ironically, Paul described his disability as a "gift." Paul had learned through his thorn to dig deeper for the blessing of his "gift" and tried not to focus on the surface appearance of his suffering. From James 1:17 we see that he had learned that "every good and perfect gift is from above." His thorn enabled his focus to shift from his irritations and onto his Savior.

So many times in life we ask the wrong question. In times of suffering or trial we tend to ask, "Why God?" when instead, we should be asking God, "How can this ordeal lift You up and give You glory?" Like the apostle Paul, we may need to change our perspective about those thorns and irritations in our life.

Paul's "thorn in the flesh" was instrumental in changing his outlook about his trials. Paul began to realize how his thorn was being used to refocus his thoughts off of himself and onto the goodness of God. Paul was able to redirect his focus from the things he could boast about to the weaker things that made him more dependent on God. For us, we must learn to look deeper than insomnia to the bigger picture of God working to change us more into the image of His Son, Jesus.

Sufficient Grace

Notice in the Second Corinthians passage that God does not provide deliverance for Paul from his discomforting irritation. God doesn't even provide Paul with an explanation; however, God abundantly provides enough grace to endure the suffering. In other words, the resources to endure were freely given to Paul.

God always give us exactly what we need to endure our trial. In regard to your insomnia, He will provide you with enough sleep to allow you to function throughout the day. God showed Paul that His grace was "sufficient". It was just enough for him to get by. God promised to supply all our needs—not wants—according to His riches in glory in Christ Jesus. [5] "Yet this I call to mind and therefore I have hope: because of the Lord's great love we are not consumed, for his compassions never fail. They are new every morning; great is your faithfulness. I say to myself, 'The Lord is my portion; therefore I will wait for him.'" [6]

We must realize that God's mercies and compassion for His children are new every morning. No matter how much tossing and turning the night brings, every morning God promises to provide us with mercies and sufficient grace to carry out the plans that He has planned for us that day. We must learn to echo the psalmist in proclaiming that "weeping may last for the night, but a shout of joy comes in the morning." [7]

Perfect Power

Because of God's unwillingness to take away the thorn, Paul became increasingly motivated to depend on God more fully, to seek Him more earnestly, and to trust Him more completely. Paul's weakness actually provided the access he needed to God's heavenly strength. Had Paul never experienced this frailty, he would not have had the need to seek, and rely upon, God's power to get through every day. Instead of dealing with our sleep issues solely through our own strength and understanding, we must learn to give God room for His grace to intervene. We must learn to seek God's intervention with our sleep issues and rely on His strength and sufficiency.

In Psalm 77 the writer languishes on his bed in the nighttime hours. We see the psalmist's example of how to deal with insomnia.

> I cried out to God for help; I cried out to God to hear me.
>
> When I was in distress, I sought the Lord; at night I stretched out untiring hands and my soul refused

to be comforted. I remembered you, O God, and I groaned; I mused and my spirit grew faint. You kept my eyes from closing; I was too troubled to speak.

I thought about the former days, the years of long ago; I remembered my songs in the night. My heart mused and my spirit inquired: will the Lord reject forever? Will he never show his favor again? Has his unfailing love vanished forever?

Has his promise failed for all time? Has God forgotten to be merciful? Has he in anger withheld his compassion? Then I thought, "To this I will appeal: the years of the right hand of the Most High." I will remember the deeds of the Lord; yes, I will remember your miracles of long ago.

I will meditate on all your works and consider all you mighty deeds. Your ways, O God, are holy. What god is so great as our God? You are the God who performs miracles; you display your power among the peoples. With your mighty arm you redeemed your people, the descendants of Jacob and Joseph. Selah.

The waters saw you, O God, the waters saw you and writhed; the very depths were convulsed. The clouds poured down water, the skies resounded with thunder; your arrows flashed back and forth. Your thunder was heard in the whirlwind, your lightning lit up the world; the earth trembled and quaked. Your path led through the sea, your way through the mighty waters, though your footprints were not seen. [8]

Reaching out to God

Asaph, the discouraged writer of the above psalm, shows many of the symptoms of depression. Just as with Paul's thorn in the flesh, we have no idea what his problem was. It may have been a fractured relationship or a recent tragedy in his life. Perhaps he was suffering the grief of a chronic illness such as cancer or arthritis. Whatever the case, discouragement became his bedfellow. In his desperation, he cried out to God for help.

Reaching out to God is the best strategy that we have in these situations. Notice the emotion and intensity of the psalmist's appeal, his cries for help. His difficulty seems to have many manifestations. His soul would not be comforted. His spirit grew faint. His hands would not grow tired from reaching out in continuous prayer, and he was so troubled that he could not even speak. But worst of all, God would not allow his eyes to shut. Asaph understood just how desperate his circumstances were, and he went to the source that could help him.

Questioning God

On his bed, Asaph remembers God—and he groans. Have you ever felt that way towards God? The writer asks a lot of tough questions in his despair. God have you rejected me?

God, do you not keep your promises? Have you forgotten to be merciful to me? Are you angry with me, God? God of course knows the uncertainties in our hearts, even if they are not verbalized. Although God doesn't owe us an explanation, He is more than able to handle our misgivings and questions. It's okay for us to be real with God about our doubts and insecurities, our anger and disillusionments, our needs and our fears that assault our minds and hearts as we toss and turn in our beds. He knows all about them anyway.

Reflecting on past experiences

Asaph began to remember his past experiences with God and the many ways God had been faithful to him in the past. He remembered his songs in the night and the years of being on God's right hand. Think back on the times that God came through for you. As we recall how He has comforted and delivered us through tough times in our past, it feeds our faith. As we recall how God has seen us through past difficulties, it becomes easier to trust His sovereignty and goodness through the current obstacles we face.

Remembering God's character

The psalmist then remembered the deeds and the miracles that God performed for the nation of Israel. Think of all the Old Testament examples of God performing great deeds and miracles for His people when they were in need. Asaph recalled God's holiness and distinctness, His mighty arm ready to redeem His people and the miracles that God was able to perform before the nations. These attributes spurred him to refocus his attention onto God.

Refocusing on God's goodness

The psalmist intentionally refocused his thoughts onto God's attributes. It became a repetitive act of the will: "I will appeal"; "I will remember"; "I will meditate." Asaph made a choice to take his eyes off whatever was tormenting his sleep, and instead, train them onto God and His goodness. This is perhaps the hardest step we have to take in our journey towards God.

Sometimes it seems there is an enormous chasm separating our feelings of grief, doubts and questions to believing God and His promises. Fortunately the journey across that seemingly endless span is made one step at a time. However, the first step can only begin when we choose to refocus in the direction of God's goodness and sovereignty.

Relying on God's Deliverance

In the rest of the psalm, Asaph thinks about how God showed Himself strong to the nation of Israel. He personally reflected on Israel's Red Sea experience. "Your path led through the sea, your way through the mighty waters, though your footprints were not seen." [9] As Israel approached the Red Sea, there didn't seem to be a way out. With pharaoh behind them, the sea in front of them, and walls on both sides, they were trapped. But

God miraculously made a way for them even though His "footprints" could not be seen at the time. God had already planned a path of deliverance.

The enduring heart understands that God will deliver—if not in this life, then for sure when we experience perfection in heaven. The challenge is knowing when and how to transfer one's faith from deliverance in this world to the next. Ultimately, a heart can endure when the expectation of heaven is kept in view.

John Cameron's *Avatar* has recently become the biggest box office hit of all time. Set in the future, a greedy corporation from resource-ravaged Earth begins mining for the costly "unobtainium" on the planet of Pandora. Unlike the impoverished, dying Earth, Pandora is a utopian fantasyland of wonder and perfection. After seeing this presentation of virtual reality, many of the viewers have started suffering from "post-*Avatar* blues." One viewer noted: "When I woke up after watching *Avatar* for the first time yesterday, the world seemed … gray. It was like my whole life, everything I've done and worked for, lost its meaning."

The movie has hit a spiritual nerve. *Avatar* has impressed upon moviegoers the longing for a better world. Embedded in the heart of every human on this planet is an innate understanding of imperfection in ourselves and the world we live in. God's promise of heaven is more than a "virtual" experience—it is a reality that the believer longs for in earnest, confident expectation.

"If I find in myself a desire which no experience in this world can satisfy, the most probable explanation is that I was made for another world."

C. S. Lewis
Mere Christianity

Living with the expectation of heaven completely transforms our perspective on insomnia and sleep. In heaven, sleep may very well be obsolete. Our mortal, corruptible bodies will have put on immortality. [10] We shall see God as He is, for we will be like Him.[11] In the Eternal City, there will be no more night, no sun or moon, and we will live in the constant, eternal, glorious presence of God. [12] There will be no sunset, no twilight, and no dawn. The old order will pass away and the new will come.

As believers, we can only imagine what we will experience in heaven, worshiping around the Throne with the angels, continuously singing "Holy, holy, holy!" It's probably an understatement to say that sleep will not be as high on our list of priorities in eternity as it is in our present condition. We will probably not want to miss a second of eternity in the presence of almighty God.

In the meantime, our purpose on this earth is to live in preparation for heaven. We must learn to glorify God in every area of our life, for in heaven, glorifying God is all we will do for all eternity. For now we live within the constraints of our mortal bodies. If we presently suffer with sleep issues, if we experience frustration when we cannot sleep, if we groan inwardly for sweet, pleasant, refreshing sleep, it's only a reminder that we have not yet arrived at our final destination. For believers, God will someday liberate us from the bondage of our decaying bodies and bring us into the glorious freedom of eternity. This is the hope that we have in Christ.

How does understanding the reality of heaven change your perspective towards your sleep issues?

173

I consider that our present sufferings are not worth comparing with the glory that will be revealed in us. The creation waits in eager expectation for the sons of God to be revealed. For the creation was subjected to frustration, not by its own choice, but by the will of the one who subjected it, in hope that the creation itself will be liberated from its bondage to decay and brought into the glorious freedom of the children of God.

We know that the whole creation has been groaning as in the pains of childbirth right up to the present time. Not only so, but we ourselves, who have the firstfruits of the Spirit, groan inwardly as we wait eagerly for our adoption as sons, the redemption of our bodies. For in this hope we were saved. [13]

The expectation of heaven motivates us to turn to God as we lay down to sleep. Heaven is more than a bedtime story, a fairy tale or a lullaby. Heaven is a reality. An enduring heart holds to this promise of deliverance and waits for the day when the walk by faith will become a walk of observation and sight.

CHAPTER 17
BALIN JAM

Balin jam ("may you pass your night in peace")—it's how the Fulani people of western Africa say goodbye. This Fulani expression best captures the message of this book. Passing your night in peace, from a biblical perspective, involves a whole lot more than sleeping well. It encompasses surrendering every aspect of sleep to God. The prerequisite for having peace as we lay down to sleep is a growing, vibrant relationship with God. Everything in our lives, including sleep, flows out of our pursuit of our loving Father in Heaven. The ability to sleep is a multifaceted gift given by God, who likewise pursues a love relationship with every individual on this planet.

From God's perspective, sleep (or its absence) is a tool designed to help fulfill His agenda in our lives and in His world. Our response should be twofold. First, we must transfer our focus off our personal sleep issues and onto the Shepherd of sleep. We must fix our eyes on Jesus, the author and finisher of our faith. Second, we need to relinquish control of sleep and allow God to shape our hearts into His image. In so doing, we may find that we sleep better.

"There is an appointed time for everything. And there is a time for every event under heaven." [1] A life of surrendered sleep is characterized by the ability to discern the time and seasons which God has prepared for us, and respond with a heart of thankfulness and obedience.

At times we may experience peaceful sleep because we are pursuing a wise heart. Let it propel us on to greater heights of service. When we encounter storms that threaten to steal our sleep, let us cling to God's presence and promises with a calm heart. If disobedience presents itself in our sleep patterns, we must return to the One who removes our sin as far as the east is from the west. If God interrupts our sleep to call, instruct or intervene in our lives, our hearts must respond in obedience.

Similarly, there are times when we must offer up to God a sacrifice of our sleep. And last, if we suffer intractable insomnia and unrest, let us move forward with a peace that passes all understanding. For an enduring and expectant heart knows that our reward and perfection is waiting just around the bend.

Surrender your heart to the One whose eyes never close. Allow Him to keep you and help you to "pass your nights in peace."

Balin jam!

About the Author...

Searching for insight into his own sleep issues, Dr. Charles Page found numerous volumes that spoke to the physical aspect of insomnia, but nothing on the spiritual dimension of insomnia. Like many doctors who are on call 24-hours a day, Dr. Page is a sleep-deprived surgeon living in Texas. He received a bachelor of arts degree in biology from Austin College in Sherman, Texas. He attended Baylor College of Medicine in Houston, Texas for his medical school and surgery residency. He currently practices medicine in Nacogdoches, Texas.

He has been happily married to Joanna for fifteen years and is the father of five children: Jacob, Jonathan, Georgia Anne, Jane Aubrey and Charlie.

Next in the Surrendered Sleep series, a new devotional and journal that will provide a more in-depth study of our relationship with our Creator.

Coming Soon!!
Surrendered Sleep: Encounters with the Shepherd Who Never Slumbers

If you found this book valuable, please let us know by posting a positive review for it on Amazon.com or Surrenderedsleep.com

APPENDIX "A"
END NOTES
CHAPTER ONE:
THE LORD OF SLEEP

1. National Sleep Foundation. *Sleep in America* polls. Washington, D.C., 2002, 2006, 2009.
2. The Barna Group, "Americans Just Want a Good Night of Sleep" October 13, 2006, *Barna.org, http://www.barna.org/barna-update/article/13-culture/145-americans-just-want-a-good-night-of-sleep?q=2006+sleep* (April 21, 2010)
3. Revelation 21:1-4
4. Psalm 121:3-6
5. Psalm 17:3
6. Psalm 139:11-12
7. S. Campbell. and I. Tobler, "Animal Sleep: A Review of Sleep Duration Across Phylogeny," *Neuroscience and Biobehavioral Review* Volume 8, Issue 3 (Autumn 1984): 269-300.
8. Genesis 1:4-5 (*emphasis the author's*)
9. Psalm 19:1-2 NAS
10. Genesis 2:21-23
11. Genesis 15:12
12. Genesis 28:13-15
13. Exodus 12
14. Judges 6:36-40
15. Ruth 3:7-12
16. Psalm 3:5
17. I Kings 19:3-8
18. Isaiah 37:33-37
19. II Kings 6:13-18
20. Jeremiah 31:26
21. Luke 2:8-20
22. Psalm 127:2 KJV (*emphasis the author's*)

23. Matthew 7:9-12
24. James 1:16-17
25. Romans 8:31-32 *(emphasis the author's)*
26. Psalm 84:11
27. I Samuel 16:7b NKJV
28. Proverbs 4:23
29. Jeremiah 17:9 NKJV
30. Hebrews 4:12 NKJV *(emphasis the author's)*

CHAPTER TWO:
A CALM HEART: INTRODUCTION

1. Acts 12:1-7
2. 1 Peter 5:7
3. Mark 4:35-41
4. Hebrews 11:6

CHAPTER THREE:
A CALM HEART: TRUST IN GOD

1. 1 Corinthians 13:11
2. 1 Peter 5:7
3. Mark 4:35
4. 2 Kings 6:14-19
5. Psalm 91:5, 11
6. Psalm 4:8
7. Psalm 3:5-6

CHAPTER FOUR:
A CALM HEART: A PROCESS OF BELIEF

1. Acts 16:22-26 NKJV
2. Romans 5:3-4 NKJV
3. James 1:2-4 NKJV
4. Hebrews 12:11 NKJV
5. Psalm 1:2
6. Psalm 4:4
7. Psalm 63:6
8. Psalm 119:148
9. Psalm 22:3 KJV
10. Hebrews 13:15 NAS
11. Psalm 34:1
12. Philippians 4:4 NAS
13. I Thessalonians 5:16-18 NAS
14. Job 35:10
15. Psalm 16:11
16. Psalm 42:8
17. Psalm 63:5-7
18. Hebrews 4:16
19. Philippians 4:6-9
20. I John 5:14-15
21. John 17-22-23
22. Galatians 2:20
23. Ephesians 1:19
24. Ephesians 3:20-21
25. Ephesians 3:20

CHAPTER FIVE:
A WISE HEART: PRIORITIES

1. Proverbs 3:1-6
2. Proverbs 3:21-24
3. James 1:5
4. Proverbs 3:5-6

CHAPTER SIX:
A WISE HEART: DAILY PURSUIT OF GOD

1. Psalm 63:1-8 NKJV
2. Matthew 22:37
3. Matthew 22:39

CHAPTER SEVEN:
A WISE HEART: RELATIONSHIPS

1. Arterburn, Steve. *Regret-Free Living*. Minneapolis: Bethany House Publishers, 2009
2. Genesis 3:12 (*emphasis the author's*)
3. Ephesians 4:26

CHAPTER EIGHT:
A WISE HEART: WORK

1. Colossians 3:23-24
2. Psalm 127 NIV
3. Philippians 4:11 KJV
4. Philippians 4:19 (*author's paraphrase*)
5. Matthew 11:28-29

CHAPTER NINE:
A WISE HEART: FINANCIAL CHOICES

1. Matthew 6:19-34
2. Psalm 50:12b
3. Philippians 4:11-12

CHAPTER TEN:
A WISE HEART: PHYSICAL ACTIVITY AND DIET

1. Ecclesiastes 5:12
2. Proverbs 23:20-21 NIV

CHAPTER ELEVEN:
A WISE HEART: A PROACTIVE APPROACH TO HEALTH

1. Luke 10:22
2. John 9:7
3. Genesis 2:7
4. National Sleep Foundation. *Sleep in America* polls. Washington, D.C., 2002, 2006, 2009.
5. 2 Chronicles 16:12
6. Rice, John R., *Prayer: Asking and Receiving* Murfreesboro, Tennessee: Sword of the Lord Publishers, 2000.

CHAPTER TWELVE:
A RESPONSIVE HEART

1. 1 Samuel 3:1-10
2. *He Knows My Name.* Tommy Walker. Copyright: © 1996 Doulos Publishing/BMI (Administered by Music Services) All Rights Reserved Used by Permission

3. John 10:3b-4
4. I Samuel 3:19-21
5. Luke 9:28-33

CHAPTER THIRTEEN:
A DISOBEDIENT HEART

1. Jonah 1:1-6
2. Judges 16:15-21
3. Proverbs 20:13
4. Proverbs 6:6-11
5. I Peter 5:8
6. Matthew 26:36-46
7. John 13:25-30

CHAPTER FOURTEEN:
A SERVANT'S HEART

1. John 17:13-20
2. Luke 6:12-20
3. Matthew 14:22-25
4. Luke 9:28-36
5. Mark 1:32-39
6. Wiersbe, Warren W. *The Best of A.W. Tozer: Volume 1* "Born after midnight" (Baker Books, 1978) p37.
7. Ibid. p39.
8. Acts 16:25-34
9. Acts 20:7-12

CHAPTER FIFTEEN:
A SEPARATED HEART

1. Shakespeare, William *Henry IV*, Part 2, Act III, Scene 1. 1597
2. Daniel 2:1-13 CEV
3. 2 Peter 3:9
4. McDowell, Josh. *The New Evidence that Demands a Verdict.* Nashville: Thomas Nelson Publishers, 1999
5. Acts 16:30
6. Acts 16:31

CHAPTER SIXTEEN:
AN ENDURING HEART

1. Psalm 77:4 NKJV
2. Job 7:3-5, 13-16
3. Job 38:4 NKJV
4. 2 Corinthians 12:7-10
5. Philippians 4:19
6. Lamentations 3:21-24
7. Psalm 30:5b NAS
8. Psalm 77:1-15
9. Psalm 77:19
10. 1 Corinthians 15: 52-54
11. I John 3:2-3
12. Revelation 21:22-26
13. Romans 8:18-24

CHAPTER SEVENTEEN:
BALIN JAM

1. Ecclesiastes 3:1 NAS

SLEEP DIARY

	DAY 1	DAY 2	DAY 3	DAY 4	DAY 5	DAY 6	DAY 7	Things That Trigger Insomnia
How long does it take you to fall asleep?	___ mins ___ hours	___ mins ___ hour	___ mins ___ hour	___ mins ___ hour	___ mins ___ hour	___ mins ___ hour	___ mins ___ hour	These are things that can affect the quality of your sleep. Check the ones that have affected you.
On a scale of 1 to 5, how do you feel when you wake up?	☐ 1 - Groggy ☐ 2 ☐ 3 ☐ 4 ☐ 5 - Rested	☐ 1 - Groggy ☐ 2 ☐ 3 ☐ 4 ☐ 5 - Rested	☐ 1 - Groggy ☐ 2 ☐ 3 ☐ 4 ☐ 5 - Rested	☐ 1 - Groggy ☐ 2 ☐ 3 ☐ 4 ☐ 5 - Rested	☐ 1 - Groggy ☐ 2 ☐ 3 ☐ 4 ☐ 5 - Rested	☐ 1 - Groggy ☐ 2 ☐ 3 ☐ 4 ☐ 5 - Rested	☐ 1 - Groggy ☐ 2 ☐ 3 ☐ 4 ☐ 5 - Rested	☐ Stress-includes family, work, finances, life changes
How many times did you wake up last night?								☐ Diet-spicy foods, alcohol, caffeine, heavy meal before bed
How many hours of sleep did you get?								☐ Lifestyle-smoking, exercise before bed, schedule changes
On a scale of 1 to 5, how do you feel during the day?	☐ 1 - Tired ☐ 2 ☐ 3 ☐ 4 ☐ 5 - Energetic	☐ 1 - Tired ☐ 2 ☐ 3 ☐ 4 ☐ 5 - Energetic	☐ 1 - Tired ☐ 2 ☐ 3 ☐ 4 ☐ 5 - Energetic	☐ 1 - Tired ☐ 2 ☐ 3 ☐ 4 ☐ 5 - Energetic	☐ 1 - Tired ☐ 2 ☐ 3 ☐ 4 ☐ 5 - Energetic	☐ 1 - Tired ☐ 2 ☐ 3 ☐ 4 ☐ 5 - Energetic	☐ 1 - Tired ☐ 2 ☐ 3 ☐ 4 ☐ 5 - Energetic	☐ Bedroom-noise, light, temperature, bedding, television in bedroom
How many naps did you take today?								☐ Spiritual-feelings of isolation from God, spiritual battles, Holy Spirit's conviction of sin
What medications are you taking?								☐ Medical-pain medicine, medications chronic ailments, vitamins and herbs